Human Biology Support Manual

First-Time Teaching Tips
and
Visual Lecture Outline

Belk | Borden

Human Biology

Benjamin Cummings

San Francisco   Boston   New York
Cape Town   Hong Kong   London   Madrid   Mexico City
Montreal   Munich   Paris   Singapore   Sydney   Tokyo   Toronto

Acquisitions Editor: Gary Carlson
Editorial Assistant: Kaci Smith
Managing Editor: Deborah Cogan
Production Supervisor: Mary O'Connell
Manufacturing Buyer: Michael Penne
Marketing Manager: Gordon Lee
Supplement Cover Designer: 17th Street Studios
Main Text Cover Designer: Studio A
Cover Photograph: Getty Images/Jimmy Chin
Design and Composition: Progressive Publishing Alternatives

ISBN-10: 0-321-59494-0
ISBN-13: 978-0-321-59494-5

Benjamin Cummings
is an imprint of

1 2 3 4 5 6 7 8 9 10 — TCS — 12 11 10 09 08

www.pearsonhighered.com

Table of Contents

The Scientific Method: Proven Effective

1

Chapter at a Glance

1.1 An Introduction to the Scientific Process
1.2 Hypothesis Testing
1.3 Understanding Statistics
1.4 Evaluating Scientific Information

Visual Lecture Outline

1.1 An Introduction to the Scientific Process

A. The Nature of Hypotheses
- Science is a process of testing hypotheses; a hypothesis is a tentative fact or proposed explanation for one or more observations.
- Scientific hypotheses must be testable and falsifiable.

B. Scientific Theories
- A scientific theory is an explanation of a set of related observations based on multiple hypothesis tests.

C. The Theory of Evolution and the Theory of Natural Selection

D. The Logic of Hypothesis Testing
- Hypotheses are often generated via inductive reasoning.
- Hypotheses are tested through the process of deductive reasoning.

Key Terms: biology; deductive reasoning; falsifiable; hypothesis; inductive reasoning; prediction; scientific method; scientific theory; supernatural; testable

Instructor Resources in Teaching Toolbox: Chapter 1 PPT slides; TAs 1–4; *Human Biology Animations:* "The Scientific Method," "Signs of Life"

Figures and Tables:

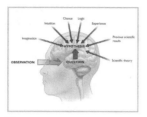

Figure 1.1
Hypothesis Generation

Figure 1.2a
Scientific Breakthrough

Figure 1.2b

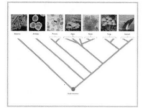

Figure 1.3
Theory of Evolution

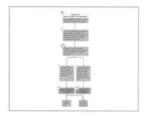

Figure 1.4
Scientific Method

1.2 Hypothesis Testing

- Absolutely proving hypotheses is impossible. However, well-designed scientific experiments can allow researchers to strongly infer that their hypothesis is correct.

A. The Experimental Method

- In an experiment, scientists manipulate an independent variable in order to measure the dependent variable.

B. Controlled Experiments

- Controlled experiments compare a randomly assigned experimental group with a control group.

C. Minimizing Bias in Experimental Designs

- Bias in scientific results can be minimized with double-blind experiments.

D. Using Correlation to Test Hypotheses

- Some hypotheses can be tested using correlation, in which scientists look for a relationship between two factors.

- A correlation can show a relationship between two factors, but it does not eliminate all alternative hypotheses; correlation does not equal causation.

Key Terms: bias; control; controlled experiment; correlation; data; dependent variable; double-blind; experiment; independent variable; model organism; placebo; random assignment; variable; *x*-axis; *y*-axis

Instructor Resources in Teaching Toolbox: Chapter 1 PPT slides; TAs 5–7, 11

In-Class Activity: Scientific Method: Put the student's knowledge of the material covered so far into practice. Divide the class into small groups (mention that science is quite often a collaborative effort) and give each group an observation or a statement that may or may not be accurate. Examples could include mosquitoes bite some people more than others, moss grows preferentially on the north side of trees, or left-handed people have better manual dexterity than right-handers. Each group should formulate a testable hypothesis based on the observation or statement and design an experiment to assess their hypothesis. If time allows, some groups could be asked to share their work with the class. Some entertaining observations and experiments will turn up.

Figures and Tables:

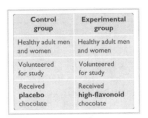

Figure 1.5
Controlled Experiment

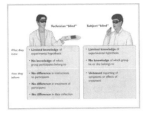

Figure 1.6
Double-Blind Experiments

Figure 1.7
Model Organisms in Science

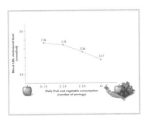

Figure 1.8
Correlation Between Diet and Cholesterol Level

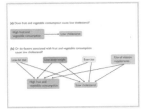

Figure 1.9
Correlation Does Not Signify Causation

Table 1.1
Types of Epidemiologic Studies

1.3 Understanding Statistics

A. What Statistical Tests Can Tell Us

- Statistics help scientists evaluate the results of their experiments by determining whether results appear to reflect the true effect of an experimental treatment on a sample of a population.

B. Statistical Significance: A Definition

- A statistically significant result is one that is very unlikely to be due to chance differences between the experimental and the control group.
- A statistical measure of the amount of variability in a sample can be expressed as the standard error, which is used to generate the confidence interval.

C. Factors Influencing Statistical Significance

- Sample size has an effect on statistical significance.

D. What Statistical Tests Cannot Tell Us

Key Terms: confidence interval; probability; sample; sample size; sampling error; standard error; statistical significance; statistics

Instructor Resources in Teaching Toolbox: Chapter 1 PPT slides; TAs 8–9

Figures and Tables:

Figure 1.10
Statistics Evaluate a Snapshot
of the Population

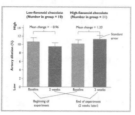

Figure 1.11
Interpreting Data from Graphs

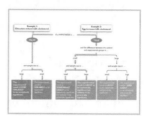

Figure 1.12
Factors that Influence
Statistical Significance

1.4 Evaluating Scientific Information

- Primary sources of information are experimental results published in professional journals and peer reviewed by other scientists before publication.

- Most people get their scientific information from secondary sources such as the news media.

A. Information from Anecdotes

- Anecdotal evidence is based on an individual's personal experience and is an unreliable means of evaluating information.

B. Science in the News

- The source of media reports must be considered when evaluating information.

C. Understanding Science from Secondary Sources

- Stories about science should be carefully evaluated for information on the actual study performed, the universality of the claims made by the researchers, and other studies on the same subject.

- Sometimes confusing stories about scientific information are a reflection of controversy within the scientific field itself.

Key Terms: anecdotal evidence; peer review

Instructor Resources in Teaching Toolbox: Chapter 1 PPT slides; TAs 10, 12; *BLAST! Tutorial:* "Evidence for Evolution: Antibiotic Resistance in Bacteria"; *ABC News Video:* "The Safety of Dietary Supplements"

Figures and Tables:

Figure 1.13
Primary Sources: Publishing
Scientific Results

Table 1.2
Guide for Evaluating Science
in the News

The Chemistry of Life: Drink to Your Health?

2

Chapter at a Glance

2.1 Water: Essential to Life

2.2 Acids, Bases, and Salts

2.3 Structure and Function of Macromolecules

2.4 Micronutrients

Visual Lecture Outline

2.1 Water: Essential to Life

- Dehydration is a decrease in the body's optimal water content.
- People, on average, lose 3 liters of water daily from their body in sweat, urine, and fecal waste.

A. The Building Blocks of Water

- A water molecule is a chemical compound of two hydrogen atoms and one oxygen atom.

B. The Structure of Water

C. Water Is a Good Solvent

- Water is a good solvent because it is a polar molecule, having a partial negative charge on one pole and a partial positive charge on the other.

D. Water Facilitates Chemical Reactions

- Water facilitates chemical reactions by allowing dissolved reactants to come in contact with each other.

E. Water Is Cohesive

F. Bottle or Tap?

Key Terms: atom; atomic number; chemical reaction; cohesion; compound; covalent bond; dehydration; electron; electron shell; electronegative; element; hydrogen bond; hydrophilic; hydrophobic; ion; ionic bond; isotope; mass number; molecule; neutron; nonpolar; nucleus; polar; product; proton; radioactive isotope; reactant; solute; solution; solvent; valence shell

Instructor Resources in Teaching Toolbox: Chapter 2 PPT slides; TAs 13–17, 31, 32; *BLAST! Tutorials:* "Covalent Bond," "Hydrogen Bonds in DNA," "Hydrogen Bonds in Water"

In-Class Activity: Surface Tension: The classic demonstration of surface tension is to place a small paper clip onto the surface of a bowl of water (bend the paper clip into a boat form with a small handle so it can be placed without disrupting the surface tension). The water's surface appears to have an almost rubbery "skin." If just a very small amount of soap is added to the water, the paper clip will immediately sink. You could challenge the students to make the paper clip float in a nonpolar liquid (it won't). Many students will have seen a variation of this at some point in their K-12 education, but it is still interesting. An Internet link to a video of the experiment is listed in the Out of Class Activities section of the Instructor Guide.

Figures and Tables:

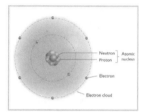

Table 2.1

Elements Found in Humans

Figure 2.1

Atomic Structure of Oxygen

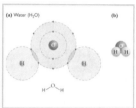

Figure 2.2

Covalent Bonding in Water

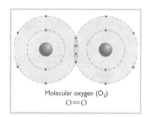

Figure 2.3

Double Covalent Bonds

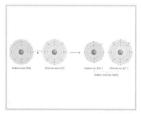

Figure 2.4

Ionic Reaction

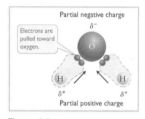

Figure 2.5

Polarity in a Water Molecule

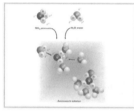

Figure 2.6

Water as a Solvent

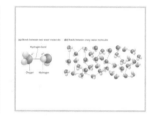

Figure 2.7

Water Is a Cohesive Substance

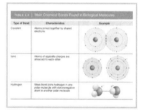

Table 2.2

Main Chemical Bonds Found in Biological Molecules

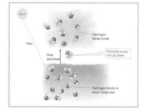

Figure 2.8

Water Absorbs Heat

Figure 2.9

Hidden Cost of Bottled Water

2.2 Acids, Bases, and Salts

A. pH: Measuring the Activity of Ions

- When a hydrogen atom loses its electron, it becomes a bare proton, also called a hydrogen ion.
- The pH scale is a measure of the relative percentages of H^+ ions in a solution and ranges from 0 (acidic) to 14 (basic).

B. Electrolytes

- Electrolytes form when substances dissociate into ions in solution and play an important role in the body by conducting electrical impulses.
- Salts are produced by the reaction of an acid with a base and are kept together via ionic bonds.

Key Terms: acid; base; buffer; electrolyte; homeostasis; pH scale; salt

Instructor Resources in Teaching Toolbox: Chapter 2 PPT slides; TA 18

Figures and Tables:

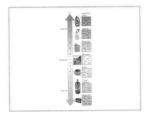

Figure 2.10
What the pH Scale Measures

2.3 Structure and Function of Macromolecules

- Organic compounds have skeletons comprised of carbon atoms.
- Macromolecules (polymers) are composed of subunits (monomers) joined together by dehydration synthesis.

A. Carbohydrates

- Carbohydrates serve as the major source of energy in cells.
- Carbohydrates can be single-unit monosaccharides or multiple-unit polysaccharides.

B. Proteins

- Proteins play enzymatic, transport, gene expression, structural, and chemical messenger roles in cells.
- Proteins are composed of amino acid monomers joined together by peptide bonds.

C. Lipids

- Lipids are hydrophobic and come in three different forms: fats, phospholipids, and steroids.

D. Nucleic Acids

- Nucleic acids are polymers of nucleotides, each of which is composed of a sugar, a phosphate, and a nitrogen-containing base (A, C, G, or T).
- DNA, the genetic material of humans, is double stranded and helical.
- RNA is involved in carrying the message of the DNA and is single stranded.

Key Terms: amino acid; antiparallel; carbohydrate; dehydration synthesis; deoxyribonucleic acid (DNA); essential amino acid; essential fatty acid; fat; fatty acid; fiber; high-density lipoprotein (HDL); hydrolysis; lipid; low-density lipoprotein (LDL); macromolecule; monomer; nitrogenous base; nucleic acid; nucleotide; organic chemistry; peptide bond; phospholipid; polymer; polysaccharide; primary structure; protein; quaternary structure; ribonucleic acid; saturated fat; secondary structure; steroid; sugar-phosphate backbone; tertiary structure; trans fat; unsaturated fat

Instructor Resources in Teaching Toolbox: Chapter 2 PPT slides; TAs 19–29, 33, 34; *BLAST! Tutorials:* "Building Proteins," "Protein Primary Structure," "Protein Secondary Structure," "Protein Tertiary and Quaternary Structure," "Unfolding and Refolding a Protein," "Alpha Helix," "Structure of DNA Double Helix"

Figures and Tables:

Figure 2.11
Carbon, the Chemical Tinkertoy Connector

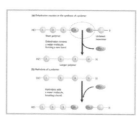

Figure 2.12
Dehydration Synthesis and Hydrolysis

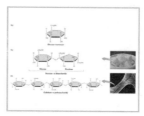

Figure 2.13
Carbohydrates

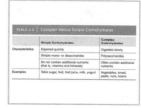

Table 2.3
Complex versus Simple Carbohydrates

Figure 2.14
Stored Carbohydrates

Figure 2.15
Which Drink Is Healthier?

Table 2.4
Amino Acids

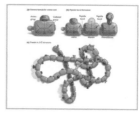

Figure 2.16
Amino Acids, Peptide Bonds, and Proteins

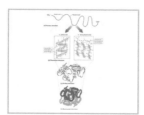

Figure 2.17
Levels of Protein Organization

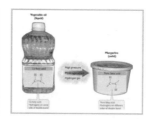

Figure 2.18
Fats

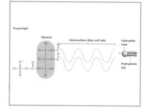

Figure 2.19
Hydrogenation

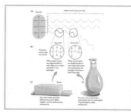

Figure 2.20
Phospholipids

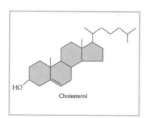

Figure 2.21
Steroids

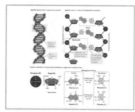

Figure 2.22
DNA Structure

2.4 Micronutrients

    A. Vitamins

        • Vitamins are organic micronutrients, most of which the body cannot synthesize.

    B. Minerals

        • Minerals are micronutrients that do not contain carbon but are essential for many cell functions.

    C. Antioxidants

        • Antioxidants are chemicals that scavenge free radicals from cells, preventing the damage these compounds can cause to other macromolecules.

    D. What Are You Paying For?

Key Terms: antioxidant; micronutrient; mineral; vitamin

Instructor Resources in Teaching Toolbox: Chapter 2 PPT slides; TAs 30, 35–38; *BLAST! Tutorials:* "Enzyme Regulation: Chemical Modification," "Enzyme Regulation: Competitive Inhibition," "How Enzymes Work: Activation Energy," "How Enzymes Work: Reaction Types and Specificity"; *ABC News Video:* "E. coli at Home"

Figures and Tables:

Figure 2.23
Vitamin D Deficiency

Table 2.5
Water-Soluble Vitamins

Table 2.6
Fat-Soluble Vitamins

Table 2.7
Minerals

Table 2.8
Antioxidants

Notes

Cell Structure and Metabolism: Diet

Chapter at a Glance

3.1 Food and Energy

3.2 Cell Structure and Function

3.3 Membrane Structure and Function

3.4 Metabolism-Chemical Reactions in the Body

3.5 Health and Body Weight

Visual Lecture Outline

3.1 Food and Energy

- Carbohydrates, proteins, and fats store energy in their chemical bonds.

- Excess energy can be stored as fat in adipose tissue.

A. ATP Is the Cell's Energy Currency

- Cells use a chemical called ATP as their energy currency.

Key Terms: adenosine diphosphate (ADP); adenosine triphosphate (ATP); adipose; phosphorylation

Instructor Resources in Teaching Toolbox: Chapter 3 PPT slides; TAs 39–43; *BLAST! Tutorials:* "Structure of ATP," "ATP / ADP Cycle"; *ABC News Video:* "Diet Meals"

Figures and Tables:

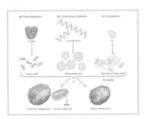

Figure 3.1
Nutrient Breakdown and Use

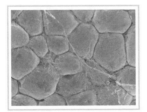

Figure 3.2
Fat Storage

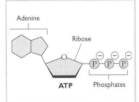

Figure 3.3
Structure of ATP

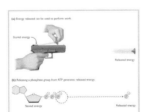

Figure 3.4
Stored Energy

Figure 3.5
Phosphorylation

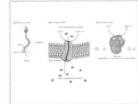

Figure 3.6
ATP and Cellular Work

3.2 Cell Structure and Function

- All living things are composed of cells.

A. Cell Structures

- Subcellular structures called organelles perform many coordinated functions in cells.

Key Terms: centriole; cytoplasm; cytoskeleton; cytosol; endoplasmic reticulum (ER); Golgi apparatus; lysosome; mitochondria; nucleus; organelle; ribosome

Instructor Resources in Teaching Toolbox: Chapter 3 PPT slides; TAs 44–50; *Human Biology Animation:* "Cell Structures"; *BioFlix:* "Tour of an Animal Cell"; *BLAST! Tutorials:* "Eukaryotic Cell Shape and Surface Area," "Surface Area to Volume Calculator," "Animal Cell Overview," "Mitochondrion"

Figures and Tables:

Figure 3.7
Cell Size

Figure 3.8
Ratios of Surface Area to Volume

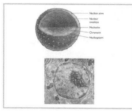

Figure 3.9
Nucleus

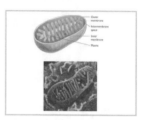

Figure 3.10
Mitochondrion

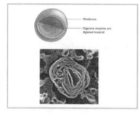

Figure 3.11
Lysosomes

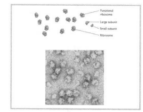

Figure 3.12
Ribosomes

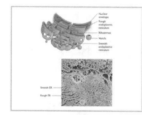

Figure 3.13
Endoplasmic Reticulum

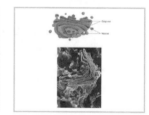

Figure 3.14
Golgi Apparatus

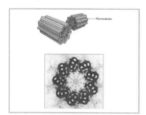

Figure 3.15
Centrioles

Figure 3.16
Cytoskeletal Elements

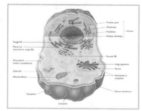

Figure 3.17
Animal Cell

3.3 Membrane Structure and Function

- Nutrients move across the plasma membrane, which functions as a semipermeable barrier that allows some substances to pass and prevents others from crossing.

A. Membrane Structure

- The plasma membrane is composed of two layers of phospholipids, in which are embedded proteins and cholesterol. Carbohydrate chains can bind to proteins and lipids on the outer surface of the membrane.

B. Transporting Substances Across Membranes

- Passive transport mechanisms include simple diffusion, osmosis, and facilitated diffusion (diffusion through proteins). Passive transport always moves substances with their concentration gradient and does not require energy.

- Active transport is an energy-requiring process that occurs when proteins in cell membranes move substances against their concentration gradients.

- In endocytosis and exocytosis, larger molecules move into and out of cells enclosed in membrane-bound vesicles.

Key Terms: active transport; diffusion; endocytosis; exocytosis; facilitated diffusion; hypertonic; hypotonic; isotonic; osmosis; passive transport; phospholipid bilayer; plasma membrane; selectively permeable; tonicity

Instructor Resources in the Teaching Toolbox: Chapter 3 PPT slides; TAs 51–55; *Human Biology Animations:* "Membrane Structure," "Passive and Active Transport," "Diffusion and Osmosis," "Endocytosis and Exocytosis"; *BioFlix:* "Membrane Transport"; *BLAST! Tutorials:* "Diffusion," "Passive Diffusion Across a Membrane," "Active Transport: Sodium-Potassium Pump," "Endocytosis and Exocytosis," "Vesicle Transport Along Microtubules"

Figures and Tables:

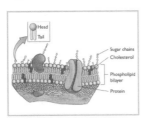

Figure 3.18
Plasma Membrane

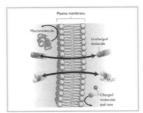

Figure 3.19
Selective Permeability

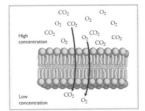

Figure 3.20
Diffusion

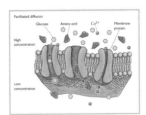

Figure 3.21
Facilitated Diffusion

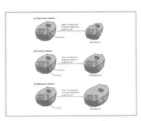

Figure 3.22
Osmosis

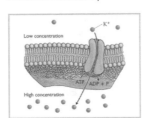

Figure 3.23
Active Transport

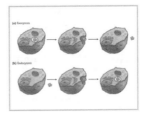

Figure 3.24
Movement of Large Substances

3.4 Metabolism—Chemical Reactions in the Body

- The chemical reactions that occur in cells to build up or break down macro-molecules are called metabolic reactions.

A. Enzymes

- Enzymes are proteins that catalyze specific cellular reactions, first by binding the substrate to the enzyme's active site. This binding causes the enzyme to change shape (induced fit), placing stress on the bonds of the substrate and thereby lowering the activation energy.

B. Cellular Respiration

- As sugars, proteins, and fats go through cellular respiration, energy stored in their chemical bonds is released and used to synthesize ATP.

C. General Overview of Cellular Respiration

- The equation for glucose breakdown is $C_6H_{12}O_6 + 6O_2 \rightarrow 6CO_2 + 6H_2O$.

D. Glycolysis, the Citric Acid Cycle, Electron Transport, and ATP Synthesis

- Cellular respiration begins in the cytosol, where a 6-carbon sugar is broken down into two 3-carbon pyruvic acid molecules during the anaerobic process of glycolysis.

- Pyruvic acid molecules then move across the two mitochondrial membranes and into the matrix of the mitochondrion, where the citric acid cycle strips them of carbon dioxide and electrons.

- Electrons are carried by electron carriers to the inner mitochondrial membrane, where they are added to a series of proteins called the electron transport chain.

- As electrons move down the electron transport chain, the energy that they release is used to drive protons into the intermembrane space. Once there, the protons rush through the enzyme ATP synthase and produce ATP from ADP and phosphate.

E. Calories and Metabolic Rate

- Energy is measured in units called Calories.
- Metabolic rate is a measure of energy use.

Key Terms: activation energy; active site; aerobic; aerobic respiration; anaerobic respiration; ATP synthase; basal metabolic rate; calorie; Calorie; catalyze; cellular respiration; citric acid cycle; electron transport chain; enzyme; fermentation; glycolysis; hydrogen atom; induced fit; metabolic rate; metabolism; nicotinamide adenine dinucleotide (NAD); pyruvic acid; specificity; substrate

Instructor Resources in Teaching Toolbox: Chapter 3 PPT slides; TAs 56–64; *Human Biology Animation:* "Breaking Down Glucose for Energy"; *BioFlix:* "Cellular Respiration"; *BLAST! Tutorial:* "Harvesting Energy: The Kreb's Cycle"

In-Class Activity: Catalase: The activity of the enzyme catalase is quickly demonstrated. Add a small piece of chicken liver to a beaker containing some hydrogen peroxide. Tremendous frothy bubbling will ensue as the catalase enzyme present in the liver converts hydrogen peroxide into water and oxygen gas.

Figures and Tables:

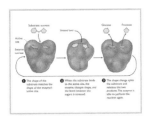

Figure 3.25
Enzymes

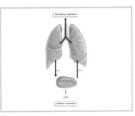

Figure 3.26
Respiration

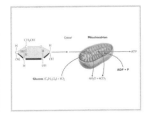

Figure 3.27
Overview of Cellular Respiration

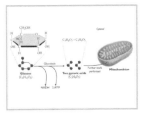

Figure 3.28
Glycolysis

Figure 3.29
NAD

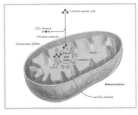

Figure 3.30
Citric Acid Cycle

Figure 3.31
Electron Transport and ADP Phosphorylation

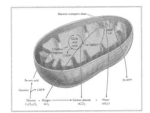

Figure 3.32
Summary of Cellular Respiration

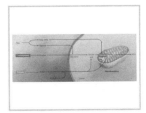

Figure 3.33
Metabolism of Other Macromolecules

Figure 3.34
Fermentation

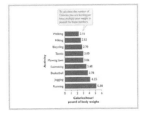

Figure 3.35
Energy Expenditures for Various Activities

3.5 Health and Body Weight

A. Underweight

- Anorexia nervosa is a disorder characterized by starvation to achieve and maintain low body weight.

- Binge eating followed by purging is called bulimia.

B. Obesity

- Both being underweight and being overweight can result in serious health consequences.

Key Terms: amenorrhea; anorexia; body mass index (BMI); bulimia; leptin; osteoporosis

Figures and Tables:

Figure 3.36
BMI

Figure 3.37
USDA Food Guide Pyramid

Genes—Transcription, Translation, Mutation, and Cloning: Genetically Modified Foods

Chapter at a Glance

4.1 What Is a Gene?
4.2 Protein Synthesis and Gene Expression
4.3 Producing Recombinant Proteins
4.4 Genetically Modified Crops

Visual Lecture Outline

4.1 What Is a Gene?

- Genes are segments of deoxyribonucleic acid (DNA) that carry information about traits that can be passed from parents to offspring.

- DNA is located within the nucleus and composed of nucleotides containing the nitrogenous bases: adenine (A), guanine (G), cytosine (C), and thymine (T).

Key Terms: chromosome; gene; genome

Instructor Resources in Teaching Toolbox: *ABC News Video:* "Genetically Modified Foods"

4.2 Protein Synthesis and Gene Expression

A. From Gene to Protein

- The main differences between RNA and DNA are that the sugar in RNA is ribose (not deoxyribose) and the nitrogenous bases are adenine, guanine, cytosine, and uracil (no thymines in RNA).

B. Transcription: Copying the Gene

- Transcription occurs in the nucleus of human cells when an RNA polymerase enzyme binds to the promoter, located at the start site of a gene, and makes the messenger RNA (mRNA) copy of the DNA gene.

C. Translation: Using the Message to Synthesize a Protein

- Translation occurs in the cytoplasm of human cells and involves mRNA, ribosomes, and transfer RNA (tRNA).

D. Mutations

- Mutations are changes to DNA sequences that can affect protein structure and function.

E. Regulating Gene Expression

- Human cells turn the expression of a gene up or down by increasing transcription in several ways: through the use of proteins that stimulate RNA polymerase binding; by varying the time that DNA spends in the uncondensed, active form; by altering the mRNA life span; by slowing down or speeding up translation; and by affecting the protein life span.

Key Terms: activator; anticodon; codon; frameshift mutation; genetic code; messenger RNA (mRNA); missense mutation; mutation; neutral mutation; nonsense mutation; point mutation; polyribosome; promoter; protein synthesis; reading frame; ribonucleic acid (RNA); ribosomal RNA (rRNA); ribosome; RNA polymerase; stop codon; transcription; transfer RNA (tRNA); translation

Instructor Resources in Teaching Toolbox: Chapter 4 PPT slides; TAs 67–76; *Human Biology Animations:* "The Structure of DNA," "The Genetic Code," "Transcription," "Translation," "Polymerase Chain Reaction (PCR)"; *BLAST! Tutorials:* "Transcription," "Translation," "DNA and RNA Compared," "Roles of RNA"

Figures and Tables:

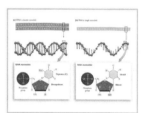

Figure 4.1
DNA and RNA

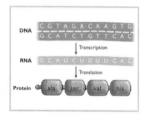

Figure 4.2
Flow of Genetic Information

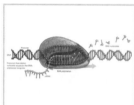

Figure 4.3
Transcription

Figure 4.4
Structure of a Ribosome

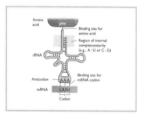

Figure 4.5
tRNA

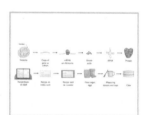

Figure 4.6
Cake Baking and Protein Synthesis

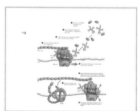

Figure 4.7
Translation

Figure 4.8
Genetic Code

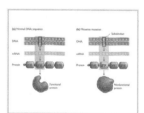

Figure 4.9
Mutation

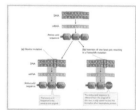

Figure 4.10
Neutral and Frameshift Mutations

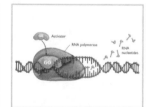

Figure 4.11
Regulation of Gene Expression by Regulating Transcription

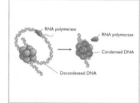

Figure 4.12
Regulating Gene Expression by Chromosome Condensation

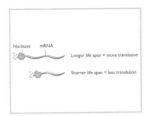

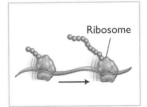

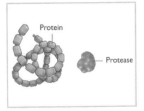

Figure 4.13
Regulating Gene Expression by Regulating mRNA Degradation

Figure 4.14
Regulating Gene Expression by Regulating Translation

Figure 4.15
Regulating Gene Expression by Regulating Protein Degradation

4.3 Producing Recombinant Proteins

- When an organism is modified to produce a new complement or arrangement of genes, the organism is said to have undergone recombination.

- Making many copies of a gene is called cloning the gene.

A. Cloning a Gene Using Bacteria

B. FDA Regulations

Key Terms: cloning; genetically modified organism (GMO); plasmid; recombination; restriction enzyme; transgenic organism

Instructor Resources in Teaching Toolbox: Chapter 4 PPT slides; TA 77; *Human Biology Animation: "Recombinant DNA"; ABC News Video:* "Human Cloning"

Figures and Tables:

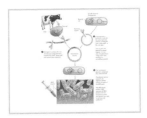

Figure 4.16
Cloning Genes Using Bacteria

4.4 Genetically Modified Crops

A. Potential Benefits of Genetically Modifying Crops

- Crop plants are genetically modified to increase their shelf life, yield, and nutritional value. They may offer a reduced environmental impact by requiring less use of chemicals such as insecticides.

B. Effect of GMOs on Human Health

- Although there have been no documented incidents of negative health effects from genetically modified food consumption, there is some concern that some genetically modified foods may cause allergic reactions or become toxins.

Instructor Resources in Teaching Toolbox: Chapter 4 PPT slides; TAs 78–79

In-Class Activity: DNA in My Food?: Take a poll of the class, asking the following question: Would you eat food that contained DNA? A large number of students may not realize that as consumers of organic matter they ingest (always have and always will) DNA in every meal. Tell them that they are not alone if they responded to the question with an answer of "no." Polls show that more than 50% of people answer "no" to this question. This a good point to show how a visceral, or reflexive, response to a question can lead us astray. Whatever the students' final perception of genetically modified foods, encourage them to make it a well-reasoned response.

Figures and Tables:

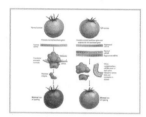

Figure 4.17
Genetically Modified
Tomatoes

Figure 4.18
Golden Rice

Figure 4.19
"No GMO" Labeling

Tissues, Organs, and Organ Systems: Work Out!

5

Chapter at a Glance

5.1 Tissues and Their Functions

5.2 Body Cavities and Membranes

5.3 Organs and Organ Systems

5.4 Homeostasis

Visual Lecture Outline

5.1 Tissues and Their Functions

A. Epithelial Tissue

- Epithelia are tightly packed tissues that line and cover organs, vessels, and body cavities.

B. Cell Junctions

- Junctions between cells serve to anchor cells to each other and allow cells to interact.

C. Connective Tissue

- Connective tissues bind tissues and organs to each other.

D. Muscle Tissue

- Muscle tissues are composed of fibers that contract and conduct electrical impulses.

E. Nervous Tissue

- Nervous tissue is composed of neurons and supporting neuroglial cells.

Key Terms: actin; adhesion junction; adipocyte; adipose tissue; astrocyte; atrophy; basement membrane; blood; bone; cardiac muscle; cartilage; chondrocyte; collagen fiber; columnar epithelium; cuboidal epithelium; dense fibrous connective tissue; elastin fiber; endocrine gland; epithelia; epithelial tissue; exocrine gland; fibroblast; gap junction; gland; ground substance; hypertrophy; intercellular junction; involuntary muscle; loose connective tissue; matrix; microglia; muscle tissue; myosin; nervous tissue; neuroglia; neuron; neurotransmitter; oligodendrocyte; osteocyte; Schwann cell; skeletal muscle; smooth muscle; squamous epithelium; striated muscle; tight junction; tissue; voluntary muscle

Instructor Resources in Teaching Toolbox: Chapter 5 PPT slides; TAs 80–85

Figures and Tables:

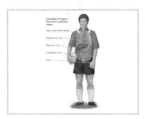

Figure 5.1
Epithelial Tissues

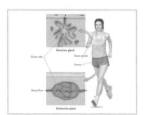

Figure 5.2
Glandular Epithelia

Figure 5.3
Types of Epithelial Tissues

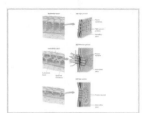

Figure 5.4
Junctions Between Cells

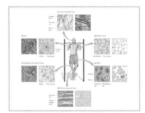

Figure 5.5
Connective Tissues

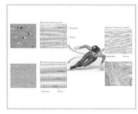

Figure 5.6
Muscle Tissue

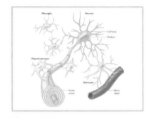

Figure 5.7
A Neuron and Neuralgia

5.2   Body Cavities and Membranes

A. Body Cavities

B. Body Membranes

- Body cavities and surfaces are lined with membranes that protect and lubricate the structures they line.

Key Terms: cutaneous membrane; diaphragm; dorsal cavity; meningeal membrane; mucous membrane; pericardium; peritoneum; pleural membrane; serous membrane; synovial membrane; ventral cavity

Instructor Resources in Teaching Toolbox: Chapter 5 PPT slides; TA 86

Figures and Tables:

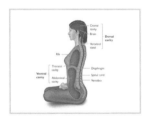

Figure 5.8
Body Cavities

Figure 5.9
Serous Membranes

5.3   Organs and Organ Systems

- Organs are groups of tissues working in concert.

A. Levels of Organization

B. Interdependence of Organ Systems

Key Terms: organ; organ system

Instructor Resources in Teaching Toolbox: Chapter 5 PPT slides; TAs 87, 91

Figures and Tables:

Table 5.1
Organs and Functions of the
Human Organ Systems

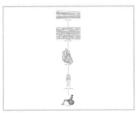

Figure 5.10
Levels of Organization

5.4 Homeostasis

- Homeostasis is the ability to maintain a relatively constant internal condition despite external fluctuations.

A. Improving Fitness

Key Terms: feedback; homeostasis; negative feedback; positive feedback; thermoregulation

Instructor Resources in Teaching Toolbox: Chapter 5 PPT slides; TAs 88–90; *Human Biology Animation:* "Homeostasis"; *BLAST! Tutorials:* "Feedback Loops," "Negative Feedback: Body Temperature," "Positive Feedback: Labor"

Figures and Tables:

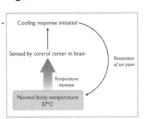

Figure 5.11
Negative Feedback

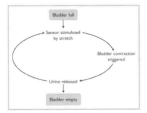

Figure 5.12
Positive Feedback

Figure 5.13
Measuring Your Heart Rate

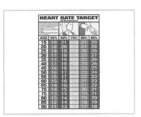

Figure 5.14
Target Heart Zone

Notes

The Skeletal, Muscular, and Integumentary Systems: Sex Differences in Athleticism

Chapter at a Glance

6.1 The Skeletal System

6.2 The Muscular System

6.3 The Integumentary System

Visual Lecture Outline

6.1 The Skeletal System

- The skeletal system is comprised of 206 bones and of connective tissues such as ligaments, tendons, and cartilage. It provides support and protection, allows for movement, and stores minerals and fat.

A. Bones of the Skeleton

B. Bone Development, Growth, Remodeling, and Repair

C. Axial Skeleton: The Central Structure

- The axial skeleton supports the trunk of the body and consists of the skull, hyoid bone, vertebral column, ribs, and sternum.

D. Appendicular Skeleton

- The appendicular skeleton is composed of the bones of the pelvic and pectoral girdles and the lower and upper limbs.

E. Joints and Movement

- Joints are regions where bones come together. Different types of joints allow for different kinds of movements.

Key Terms: abduction; acetabulum; adduction; appendicular skeleton; axial skeleton; ball-and-socket joint; calcitonin; carpal bone; chondroblast; circumduction; clavicle; compact bone; cranium; diaphysis; epiphyseal plate; epiphysis; ethmoid bone; extension; femur; fibula; flexion; frontal bone; glenoid cavity; growth plate; hinge joint; humerus; hyoid bone; ilium; intervertebral disk; ischium; lacunae; mandible; maxillae; medullary cavity; metacarpal; metatarsal; nasal bone; occipital bone; osteoblast; osteoclast; osteocytes; parathyroid hormone; parietal bone; patella; pectoral girdle; pelvic girdle; periosteum; phalanges; pivot joint; pubis; radius; red bone marrow; rib; rib cage; rotation; scapula; sinus; skull; sphenoid spongy bone; sternum; synovial joint; tarsal; temporal bone; tibia; ulna; vertebra; vertebral column; yellow bone marrow; zygomatic bone

Instructor Resources in Teaching Toolbox: Chapter 6 PPT slides; TAs 92–111; *Human Biology Animations:* "Bone Growth," "Bone Repair"

In-Class Activity: Joint Movement: Here is an opportunity to get the class out of their chairs. As you explain each type of joint movement (flexion, extension, adduction, abduction, rotation, circumduction), have students move selected joints in the appropriate fashion. The instructor can demonstrate the movements or illustrate them on a full skeleton if available.

Figures and Tables:

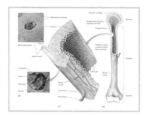

Figure 6.1
Structure of a Long Bone

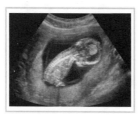

Figure 6.2
Fetal Sonogram

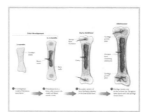

Figure 6.3
Bone Development

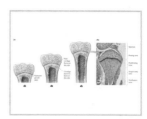

Figure 6.4
Bone Growth

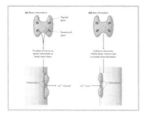

Figure 6.5
Bone Remodeling

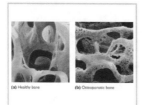

Figure 6.6
Normal and Osteoporotic Bone

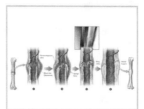

Figure 6.7
Steps in the Repair of a Fracture

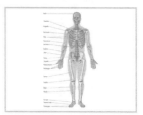

Figure 6.8
Human Skeleton

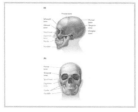

Figure 6.9
Skull Bones

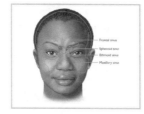

Figure 6.10
Sinuses

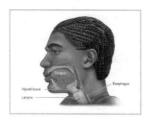

Figure 6.11
Hyoid Bone

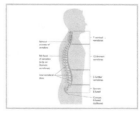

Figure 6.12
Vertebral Column

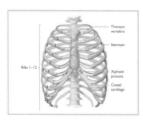

Figure 6.13
Rib Cage

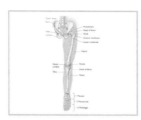

Figure 6.14
Pelvic Girdle and Lower Limb Bones

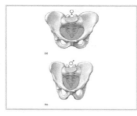

Figure 6.15
Bony Pelvis

Figure 6.16
Sex Differences in the Skeleton

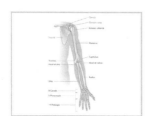

Figure 6.17
Pectoral Girdle and Upper Limb

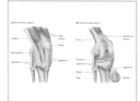

Figure 6.18
Synovial Joint

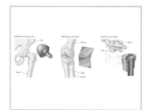

Figure 6.19
Types of Joints

Figure 6.20
Joint Movements

6.2　The Muscular System

- The three types of muscles are smooth, cardiac, and skeletal.

A. Names and Actions of Skeletal Muscles

B. Skeletal Muscle Structure

- A muscle contains bundles of muscle fibers or fascicles.

C. Skeletal Muscle Contraction

D. Energy Inputs for Muscle Contraction

Genes & Homeostasis: Muscular Dystrophy

Key Terms: actin; antagonistic muscle pair; creatine phosphate; fascia; fascicle; insertion; motor neuron; motor unit; muscle fiber; myofibril; myosin; neuromuscular junction; origin; sarcolemma; sarcomere; sarcoplasm; sarcoplasmic reticulum; sliding filament model; tropomyosin; troponin; T tubule; Z disc

Instructor Resources in Teaching Toolbox: Chapter 6 PPT slides; TAs 112–118; *Human Biology Animation:* "Muscle Structure and Function"; *BioFlix:* "Muscle Contraction"; *BLAST! Tutorials:* "Anatomy of Muscle"; *ABC News Video:* "Steroids," "The Mitchell Report"

Figures and Tables:

Figure 6.21
Antagonistic Muscle Pairs

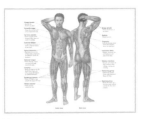

Figure 6.22
Human Skeletal Muscles

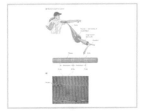

Figure 6.23
Skeletal Muscle Structure

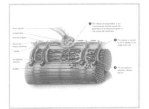

Figure 6.24
Nerve Activation of a Muscle

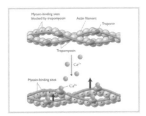

Figure 6.25
Calcium Binds Troponin

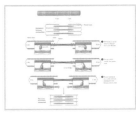

Figure 6.26
Muscle Contractions

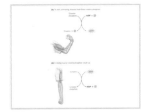

Figure 6.27
Muscle Contraction Requires Energy

6.3　The Integumentary System

- The skin functions as a protective barrier against abrasion, bacteria, ultraviolet light, and dehydration. It also helps regulate body temperature.

- The skin consists of the outer epidermis and the underlying dermis.

A. Epidermis

B. Dermis

C. Accessory Structures of the Skin

   • Accessory structures of the skin include nails, hair, sebaceous glands, and sweat glands.

D. Subcutaneous Layer

E. What Do Sex Differences Really Mean?

Key Terms: dermis; epidermis; hair; hypodermis; integumentary system; melanocyte; nail; sebaceous gland; subcutaneous layer; sweat gland

Instructor Resources in Teaching Toolbox: Chapter 6 PPT slides; TA 119

Figures and Tables:

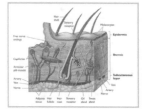

Figure 6.28
Skin Anatomy

Figure 6.29
Swimmer in a Streamline Position

The Digestive System: Weight-Loss Surgery

7

Chapter at a Glance

7.1 The Digestive Tract

7.2 Three Accessory Organs of the Digestive System

7.3 Weighing the Risks of Gastric Bypass Surgery

Visual Lecture Outline

7.1   The Digestive Tract

- Digestion is the breakdown of food into substances the body can absorb.
- Digestion involves both mechanical and chemical processes.

A. The Wall of the Digestive Tract

- The wall of the digestive tract is composed of four layers: mucosa, submucosa, muscularis, and serosa.

B. The Mouth: The Actions of Teeth and Saliva

- Saliva contains enzymes that begin the breakdown of starch and lipids.

C. The Pharynx and the Esophagus: Transport to the Stomach

- The esophagus functions to convey food to the stomach. No chemical digestion occurs in the esophagus.
- Peristalsis (rhythmic contracts of the muscularis smooth muscle layer) aids transport of materials in the digestive tract.

D. The Stomach: Digestion in an Acid Bath

- Mechanical and chemical digestion both occur in the stomach.
- Chemical digestion involves gastric juice that contains hydrochloric acid and pepsin.
- Chyme (the mix of partially digested food and gastric juice) enters the small intestine through the pyloric sphincter.

E. The Small Intestine: Where Most Digestion Happens

- The small intestine is the primary site for chemical digestion and absorption of nutrients.
- The three regions are the duodenum, jejunum, and ileum.

F. Regulation of Digestive Secretions

G. The Large Intestine: Absorption and Elimination

- The primary functions of the large intestine are absorption of water, salts, and some vitamins, as well as the formation, storage, and lubrication of fecal matter.
- The four regions are the cecum, colon, rectum, and anus.

H. Gastric Bypass Surgery: Scaling Back Digestion

- The surgery decreases the size of the stomach.
- The surgery allows food to bypass major sites of digestion and absorption.
- Many complications may arise from this procedure.

Genes & Homeostasis: Obesity

Key Terms: alimentary canal; anus; appendicitis; appendix; canine tooth; cecum; chime; colon; crown; dentin; digestion; digestive tract; duodenum; enamel; epiglottis; esophagus; fecal matter; hard palate; ileum; incisor; jejunum; large intestine; microvillus (microvilli); molar; mouth; pepsin; peristalsis; pharynx; premolar; pulp cavity; rectum; root; small intestine; soft palate; sphincter; stomach; taste bud; tonsil; tooth (teeth); villus (villi)

Instructor Resources in Teaching Toolbox: Chapter 7 PPT slides; TAs 120–130; *Human Biology Animation:* "The Digestive System"

In Class Activity: Swallow Reflex: Ask the students to swallow while touching their "Adam's apple." It gives them an appreciation for the movement of laryngeal cartilages during the swallowing reflex. Ask the students what the consequences could be from a failure of the swallowing reflex.

Figures and Tables:

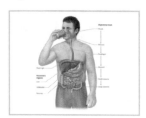

Figure 7.1
Digestive System

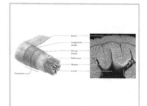

Figure 7.2
Wall of the Digestive Tract

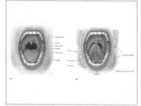

Figure 7.3
Oral Cavity

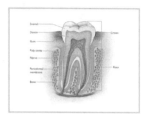

Figure 7.4
Structure of a Tooth

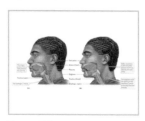

Figure 7.5
Swallowing

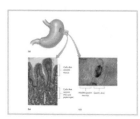

Figure 7.6
Stomach

Figure 7.7
Small Intestine Absorbs
Nutrients

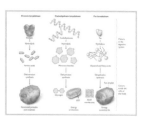

Figure 7.8
You Are What You Eat

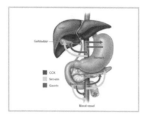

Figure 7.9
Hormonal Control of the
Digestive System

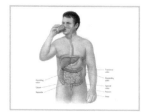

Figure 7.10
Large Intestine

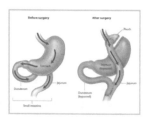

Figure 7.11
Gastric Bypass Surgery

7.2 Accessory Organs of the Digestive System

    A. Liver

    B. Gallbladder

    C. Pancreas

Key Terms: bile; bilirubin; diabetes mellitus; emulsification; gallbladder; glucagon; insulin; lipase; liver; lobules; pancreas; pancreatic amylase; sodium bicarbonate ($NaHCO_3$); trypsin; type 1 insulin-dependent diabetes mellitus (IDDM); type 2 noninsulin-dependent diabetes mellitus (NIDDM)

Instructor Resources in Teaching Toolbox: Chapter 7 PPT slides; TAs 130–133

Figures and Tables:

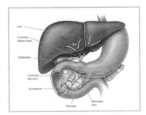

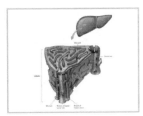

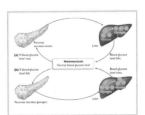

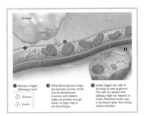

Figure 7.12
Accessory Organs of the Digestive Tract and Their Associated Ducts

Figure 7.13
Liver Lobule

Figure 7.14
Regulation of Blood-Glucose Levels

Figure 7.15
Diabetes

7.3 Weighing the Risks of Gastric Bypass Surgery

Instructor Resources in Teaching Toolbox: *ABC News Videos:* "Gastric Bypass Surgery," "Fast Food Diet"

Notes

The Blood: Malaria—A Deadly Bite

Chapter at a Glance

8.1 The Constituents of Blood

8.2 Malaria and the Blood

8.3 Blood Clotting

8.4 Ending Malaria

Visual Lecture Outline

8.1 The Constituents of Blood

A. Plasma

B. Formed Elements: The Cellular Portion of Blood

Key Terms: albumin; antibody; B lymphocyte; basophil; blood; circulatory system; eosinophil; erythrocyte; formed elements; globulin; hemoglobin; leukocyte; macrophage; malaria; megakaryocyte; monocytes; neutrophil; parasite; plasma; platelet; serum; stem cells; T lymphocyte

Instructor Resources in Teaching Toolbox: Chapter 8 PPT slides; TAs 134–137, 142; *Human Biology Animations:* "Blood," "The Life Cycle of Plasmodium"

Figures and Tables:

Figure 8.1
Circulatory System

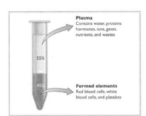

Figure 8.2
Constituents of Blood

Figure 8.3
Plasma

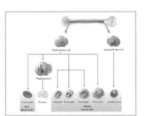

Figure 8.4
Blood Cells Arise in the Bone Marrow

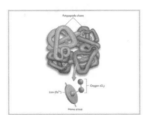

Figure 8.5
Hemoglobin

Table 8.1
White Blood Cells and Their Functions

8.2 Malaria and the Blood

    A. Malaria Infection

    B. Anemia and Blood Cell Production

    C. Blood Types and Transfusions

    D. Recycling Red Blood Cells

Key Terms: ABO system; agglutination; anemia; antigen; blood transfusion; blood type; Duffy antigen; erythropoietin; jaundice; Rh factor

Instructor Resources in Teaching Toolbox: Chapter 8 PPT slides; TAs 138–140, 143–144; *Human Biology Animation:* "Blood Types"

In-Class Activity: Encouraging Blood Donation: Consider taking time to encourage our next generation of blood donors. Poll the class on who has given blood. Ask a few students why they donated and how they feel about the experience. Students respond well to the motivations and positive experiences of their peers. Your institution may routinely schedule blood drives; alert the class to upcoming donation opportunities.

Figures and Tables:

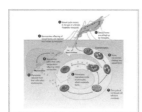

Figure 8.6
Life Cycle of *Plasmodium falciparum*

Table 8.2
Forms of Malaria

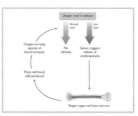

Figure 8.7
Homeostasis of Blood Oxygen

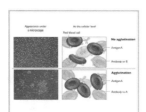

Figure 8.8
Blood Types and Antibodies

Table 8.3
Donor-Recipient Relationships in the ABO Blood System

Figure 8.9
Rh Incompatibility

8.3 Blood Clotting

    A. The Clotting Cascade

    B. Clotting Disorders

Genes & Homeostasis: Sickle-Cell Anemia

Key Terms: blood clot; embolism; fibrin; fibrinogen; hemophilia; hemorrhage; homeostasis; shock; sickle-cell anemia; thrombin; thrombosis

Instructor Resources in Teaching Toolbox: Chapter 8 PPT slides; TAs 140–141

Figures and Tables:

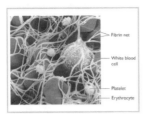

Figure 8.10
Blood Clot

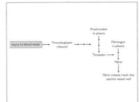

Figure 8.11
Blood Clotting

8.4 Ending Malaria

Key Terms: immunization

Instructor Resources in Teaching Toolbox: Chapter 8 PPT slides; TA 141

Figures and Tables:

Figure 8.12
A Simple Way to Reduce
Malaria

Notes

The Cardiovascular System: Can We Stop the Number-One Killer?

Chapter at a Glance

9.1 Blood and Lymphatic Vessels: The Circulation Pipes

9.2 The Mechanical Heart

9.3 The Electrical Heart

9.4 Power for the Heart

Visual Lecture Outline

9.1 Blood and Lymphatic Vessels: The Circulation Pipes

- The circulatory system consists of the blood vessels, the heart, and the lymphatic system. Its function is to transport materials and wastes around the body.

A. Arteries and Arterioles

- Arteries and arterioles carry blood from the heart.

B. Capillaries: The Distribution Network

- Capillaries are thin walled to allow the rapid exchange of materials between the body and the blood.

C. Veins: The Path Back to the Heart

- Veins are the vessels that return blood to the heart.

D. The Lymphatic System: Draining the Tissues

- The lymphatic system drains excess fluid from body tissues, returning it to veins in the vascular system.

E. Control of Blood Pressure

- Blood pressure is regulated by blood volume and arteriole diameter.

F. Fixing the Pipes

Genes & Homeostasis: Race-Based Medicine?

- Race-based medicine is a targeted approach to treatment that recognizes that individuals vary in disease susceptibility and response to drugs.

Key Terms: aneurysm; arteriole; artery; atherosclerosis; blood pressure; blood vessel; capillary; capillary bed; cardiovascular system; diastolic system; hypertension; lymph; lymph ducts; lymphatic system; precapillary sphincters; pulse; respiratory pump; sphygmomanometer; stroke; systolic pressure; veins; venules

Instructor Resources in Teaching Toolbox: Chapter 9 PPT slides; TAs 145–154, 168; *Human Biology Animation:* "The Cardiovascular System"; *BLAST! Tutorials:* "Anatomy of the Heart," "Cardiac Cycle Overview"; *ABC News Video:* "Lawsuit over Vioxx"

Figures and Tables:

Figure 9.1

Overview of the Circulatory System

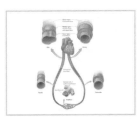

Figure 9.2

Vascular System

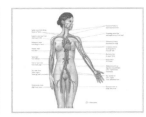

Figure 9.3

Pulse Points

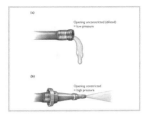

Figure 9.4

Arteriole Diameters and Blood Pressure

Figure 9.5

Tiny Blood Vessels

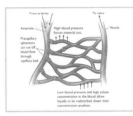

Figure 9.6

Capillary Bed

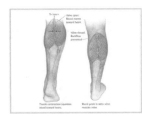

Figure 9.7

Flow of Blood in the Veins

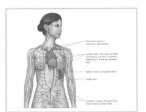

Figure 9.8

Lymphatic System

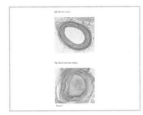

Figure 9.9

Atherosclerosis

Figure 9.10

Monitoring Blood Pressure

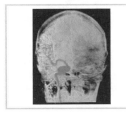

Figure 9.11

Aneurysm

Table 9.1

Drugs for Treating Heart Disease

9.2   The Mechanical Heart

A. Structure of the Heart

- The heart is a muscular pump consisting of four chambers: two atria and two ventricles.

- The chambers of the heart are connected to each other and to the circulatory system via valves, the atrioventricular and semilunar valves, which prevent the backflow of blood.

B. The Cardiovascular Pathway

- Blood pumped by the heart flows in a double circulation system. Blood ejected from the right ventricle enters the pulmonary circuit to the lungs, where it picks up oxygen. It returns to the left atrium and is forced into the left ventricle, which ejects it through the aorta into systemic circulation in the body. Blood returns to the right atrium via the veins.

C. Repairing the Pump

Key Terms: aorta; artificial hearts; atrioventricular (AV) valves; atrium; heart; heart failure; heart murmur; hepatic portal system; inferior vena cava; pericardium; pulmonary artery; pulmonary circuit; pulmonary veins; semilunar valves; superior vena cava; systemic circuit; ventricle

Instructor Resources in Teaching Toolbox: Chapter 9 PPT slides; TAs 155–159

In-Class Activity: Heart Sounds: Students love to hear heart sounds! Play a normal heart sound and then several abnormal sounds. Challenge the class to describe the difference. Play them again and point out the difference while explaining the anatomical and physiological reasons for the altered heart sound. Audio of murmurs, gallop rhythms, and the like are available online; see the Out of Class Activities section for links.

Figures and Tables:

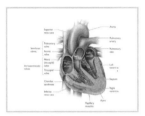

Figure 9.12
Human Heart

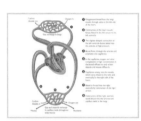

Figure 9.13
Cardiovascular System

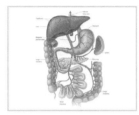

Figure 9.14
Hepatic Portal System

Figure 9.15
Stethoscope

Figure 9.16
Replacement Valves

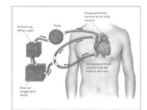

Figure 9.17
Heart-Lung Machine

9.3 The Electrical Heart

A. The Cardiac Cycle

- Contraction of the heart muscle is triggered by electrical signals from the sinoatrial (SA) node in the right atrium. These signals are transmitted to the atrioventricular (AV) node, which delays their transmission slightly so that the ventricles contract a fraction of second after the atria contract.

- Heart rate and strike volume are controlled by the negative feedback loop regulating blood pressure. The heart rate can be modified by higher-level brain functions, including intense emotions, and by certain hormones and drugs.

B. Steadying the Heartbeat

- Disruption of the heart's electrical system can lead to cardiac arrest.

Key Terms: arrhythmia; artificial pacemaker; atrioventricular (AV) node; cardiac arrest; cardiac cycle; cardiopulmonary resuscitation (CPR); defibrillators; diastole; electrocardiogram (ECG); fibrillation; myocardium; sinoatrial (SA) node; systole

Instructor Resources in Teaching Toolbox: Chapter 9 PPT slides; TAs 160–163; *BLAST! Tutorial:* "Electric Coordination of Cardiac Cycle"

Figures and Tables:

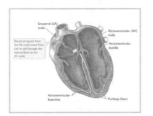

Figure 9.18
Heart's Electrical Circuit

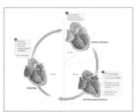

Figure 9.19
Cardiac Cycle

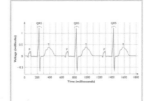

Figure 9.20
ECG

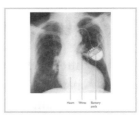

Figure 9.21
Pacemaker

9.4 Power for the Heart

A. Coronary Blood Vessels

- Coronary arteries supply blood to the heart muscle to power its energy-intensive activities.

B. Maintaining the Heart's Energy Supply

- A heart attack (myocardial infarction) occurs when blockage in a coronary artery restricts or stops blood flow.

C. A Healthy Heart

Key Terms: angina; angioplasty; cardiac veins; coronary arteries; coronary bypass surgery; coronary heart disease (CHD); heart attack; myocardial infarction

Instructor Resources in Teaching Toolbox: Chapter 9 PPT slides; TAs 164–167

In-Class Activity: Women's Heart Health: A large knowledge deficit exists concerning heart disease in women. The Out of Class Activities section has a link to a six-question online quiz. Present the quiz as a class group activity. As each true/false question is displayed, poll the class for the correct answer. Choose the consensus answer and then reveal the correct answer. The quiz reveals the scope of the issue to the students.

Figures and Tables:

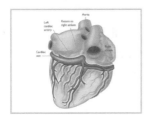

Figure 9.22
Coronary Circulation

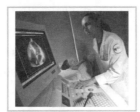

Figure 9.23
Echocardiogram

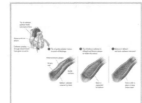

Figure 9.24
Angioplasty

Figure 9.25
Working Out the Heart Muscle

The Respiratory System: Secondhand Smoke

10

Chapter at a Glance

10.1 Respiratory System Anatomy: The Path of Smoke into the Lungs

10.2 Tobacco Smoke and the Respiratory Tract

10.3 Inhaling and Exhaling

10.4 Gas Exchange in the Lungs

10.5 Beyond the Lungs

Visual Lecture Outline

10.1 Respiratory System Anatomy: The Path of Smoke into the Lungs

A. Upper Respiratory Tract

- The upper respiratory tract consists of the mouth, nose, sinuses, and pharynx and functions to clean and condition incoming air.

B. Lower Respiratory Tract

- The lower respiratory tract consists of the larynx, trachea, bronchi, and lungs and delivers inhaled air to the respiratory surfaces in the alveoli.

Genes & Homeostasis: Did an Old Killer Spawn a New One?

- Individuals carrying a single copy of the cystic fibrosis allele may experience lower mortality rates in response to *Mycobacterium tuberculosis* infection.

Key Terms: alveoli; auditory tubes; bronchiole; bronchus; Eustachian tubes; larynx; lower respiratory tract; lungs; mouth; nasal cavity; nose; pharynx; pleural membrane; respiratory system; septum; sinus; trachea; upper respiratory tract; vocal cords

Instructor Resources in Teaching Toolbox: Chapter 10 PPT slides; TAs 169–174; *Human Biology Animation:* "The Human Respiratory System"

Figures and Tables:

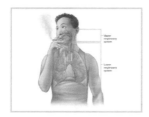

Figure 10.1
Respiratory System

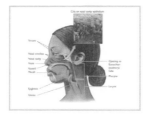

Figure 10.2
Upper Respiratory Tract

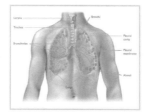

Figure 10.3
Lower Respiratory Tract

Figure 10.4
Functions of the Vocal Chords

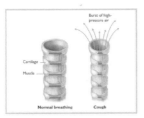

Figure 10.5
Anatomy of a Cough

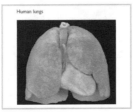

Figure 10.6
Healthy Lungs

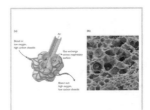

Figure 10.7
Alveoli

10.2 Tobacco Smoke and the Respiratory Tract

- Tobacco smoke comes in two forms: mainstream smoke and sidestream smoke (secondhand).

A. The Composition of Tobacco Smoke

B. Smoke Damages the Respiratory System

Key Terms: asthma; bronchitis; environmental tobacco smoke; laryngitis; otitis media; particulates; pneumonia; sinusitis; tonsillitis

Instructor Resources in Teaching Toolbox: Chapter 10 PPT slides; TAs 175-176; *ABC News Videos:* "Childhood Asthma," "Secondhand Smoke"

Figures and Tables:

Figure 10.8
Exposure to Tobacco Smoke

Figure 10.9
Asthma Treatment

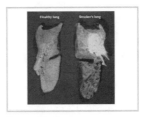

Figure 10.10
Tobacco Tar Trapped in Lungs

10.3 Inhaling and Exhaling

- Breathing facilitates external respiration, the exchange of gases between the body and the environment. External respiration is necessary to allow internal respiration, the delivery of oxygen, and removal of carbon dioxide from tissues in which cellular respiration is occurring.

A. The Mechanics of Breathing

- The tidal volume is the amount that we breathe in and out in a single breath; the vital capacity is the total that we can exhale.

- The residual volume is the remaining air that we cannot exhale.

B. The Control of Breathing

- The respiratory center of the brain controls the breathing rate under normal conditions, but this rate is modified by homeostatic processes and by the voluntary control of breathing.

C. Smoking and Breathing

- Smoke damages the alveoli and makes the lung less elastic, obstructing exhalation and interfering with normal gas exchange.

Key Terms: apnea; chronic obstructive pulmonary disease (COPD); diaphragm; emphysema; exhalation; expiration; external respiration; inhalation; inspiration; intercostal muscles; internal respiration; residual volume; respiratory center; tidal volume; ventilation; vital capacity

Instructor Resources in Teaching Toolbox: Chapter 10 PPT slides; TAs 177–183

In-Class Activity: Breathing Mechanics: Inspiration is an active process; expiration is usually passive, but can be active. Have students place a hand on their chest while breathing in. They will feel their rib cage rise as the external intercostal muscles contract. With inspiration complete, the muscles will relax and the chest will fall passively back to its prebreath position. While still touching their chest, have students forcefully exhale. The rib cage can be felt moving inward as the internal intercostal muscles contract.

Figures and Tables:

Figure 10.11
Breathing and Respiration

Figure 10.12
Lung Capacity

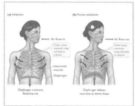

Figure 10.13
Mechanics of Taking a Breath

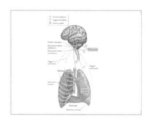

Figure 10.14
Control of Breathing

Figure 10.15
Homeostasis of Blood Gases

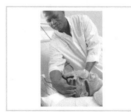

Figure 10.16
Treatment for Sleep Apnea

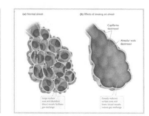

Figure 10.17
Alveoli Damage Due to Smoke Exposure

10.4 Gas Exchange in the Lungs

- The respiratory surface in humans is comprised of the walls of the alveoli. Oxygen diffuses across this surface into the capillaries, and carbon dioxide diffuses out into the alveoli.

A. A Closer Look at Gas Exchange

B. Smoking and Gas Exchange

C. Nicotine: Why Tobacco Is Habit Forming

Key Terms: gas pressure; partial pressure; respiratory surface; surfactant

Instructor Resources in Teaching Toolbox: Chapter 10 PPT slides; TAs 184–187

Figures and Tables:

Figure 10.18
Hemoglobin

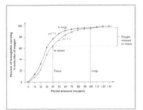

Figure 10.19
Hemoglobin Binding

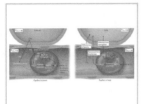

Figure 10.20
Carbon Dioxide in the Blood

Figure 10.21
Nicotine

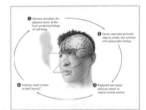

Figure 10.22
Addiction to Nicotine

10.5 Beyond the Lungs

A. The Effects of Smoke on Other Organ Systems

B. Preventing Smoking-Related Illness

Instructor Resources in Teaching Toolbox: Chapter 10 PPT slides; TAs 188–189

In-Class Activity: Smoking Questions: Asking the class questions about their experiences with smoking can lead to interesting discussions. It is important that the students feel free to discuss smoking without being judged. Question topics may include age at onset of smoking, influences on their decision to smoke, efforts to quit, and whether they consider themselves to be addicted.

Figures and Tables:

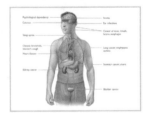

Figure 10.23
Tobacco Smoke Affects Nearly
All Organ Systems

Table 10.1
Strategies of Successful Quit
Smoking Programs

The Urinary System: Surviving the Ironman

11

Chapter at a Glance

Visual Lecture Outline

11.1 An Overview of the Urinary System

A. Homeostasis and the Urinary System

- The urinary system is responsible for excretion, the removal of wastes from the body, as well as maintaining homeostasis of a number of ions, blood pH, and blood pressure.

B. Structure of the Urinary System

- The urinary system consists of the kidneys, ureters, urinary bladder, and urethra.

C. Urination

- When the urinary bladder becomes full, the micturition reflex is triggered, causing urine to flow into the urethra.

Key Terms: elimination; excretion; external urethral sphincter; internal urethral sphincter; kidney; micturition reflex; nephrons; renal cortex; renal medulla; renal pelvis; ureter; urethra; urinary bladder; urinary system; urination

Instructor Resources in Teaching Toolbox: Chapter 11 PPT slides; TAs 190–193; *Human Biology Animation:* "The Urinary System"; *BLAST! Tutorials* "Anatomy of the Kidney," "How the Kidney Works"

Figures and Tables:

Figure 11.1
Functions of the Urinary System

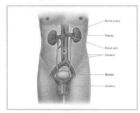
Figure 11.2
Organs of the Urinary System

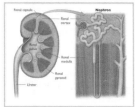
Figure 11.3
Kidneys

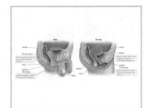

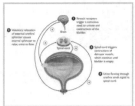

Figure 11.4
Sex Differences in the Urinary
System

Figure 11.5
Positive Feedback During
Urination

11.2 Excretion

A. The Composition of Urine

- Urine is a solution of metabolic wastes, ions, and toxins.

B. Urine Formation

Key Terms: afferent arteriole; collecting duct; distal tubule; efferent arteriole; glomerular capsule; glomerulus; nephron loop; proximal tubule; urea; urine

Instructor Resources in Teaching Toolbox: Chapter 11 PPT slides; TAs 194–199

In-Class Activity: Urinalysis: A urinalysis (UA) is a commonly used screening and diagnostic tool. A portion of a complete UA involves using urine "dipsticks," which enable the test results to be read as color changes. This portion of the UA can be easily demonstrated to the class, with a discussion of the parameters assayed by the dipstick strip and their clinical importance.

Figures and Tables:

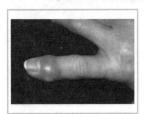

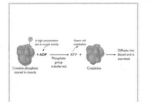

Figure 11.6
Gout

Figure 11.7
Creatinine

Figure 11.8
Ironman Mass Start

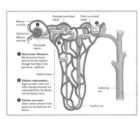

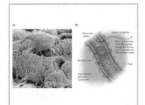

Figure 11.9
Nephron Structure and Function

Figure 11.10
Glomerular Filtration

Figure 11.11
Tubular Reabsorption

11.3 Water, pH, and Salt Balance

    A. Hormones and Water Depletion

    B. Countercurrent Exchange in the Kidney

    C. Maintaining Blood pH

    D. Salt Balance: The Right Amount of Sodium

       • The presence of salt keeps the blood isotonic to body tissues.

Genes & Homeostasis: Please Pass on the Salt

       • Scientists have identified many genes that contribute to a susceptibility to hypertension, including those involved in angiotensin production.

Key Terms: acidosis; aldosterone; angiotensin II; antidiuretic hormone (ADH); atrial natriuretic peptide (ANP); countercurrent exchange; dehydration; diuretic; hyponatremia; renin

Instructor Resources in Teaching Toolbox: Chapter 11 PPT slides; TAs 200–204

Figures and Tables:

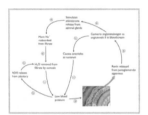

Figure 11.12
Hormones, Water Loss, and Blood Pressure

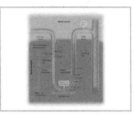

Figure 11.13
Water Conservation

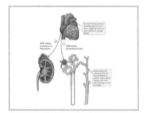

Figure 11.14
Diuretic

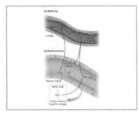

Figure 11.15
Buffers in the Blood

Figure 11.16
Effects of Hyponatremia

11.4 When Kidneys Fail

    • Irreversible damage to nephrons caused by kidney stones, infection, or chronic high blood pressure can cause a decline in kidney function.

    • Kidney function can be replaced by dialysis, which requires pumping the blood supply through semipermeable tubes immersed in a bath of clean fluid. Wastes dissolve out of the blood and into the fluid.

Key Terms: dialysis; end-stage renal disease (ESRD); kidney stone

Instructor Resources in Teaching Toolbox: Chapter 11 PPT slides; TA 205

Figures and Tables:

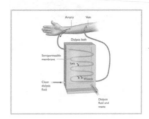

Figure 11.17
Dialysis

Figure 11.18
Managing Water Intake

Immune System: Will Mad-Cow Disease Become an Epidemic?

12

Chapter at a Glance

12.1 Infectious Agents

12.2 Transmission of Infectious Agents

12.3 The Body's Response to Infection: The Immune System

12.4 Preventing an Epidemic of Prion Diseases

Visual Lecture Outline

12.1 Infectious Agents

- Infections result from invasion and multiplication of pathogens.

- Organisms that benefit from a relationship with a host, but that contribute nothing of benefit to the host, are parasites.

A. Bacteria

- Bacteria cause disease by using the host's resources to reproduce rapidly and by releasing toxins into the host.

Genes & Homeostasis: Mutations and Development of Antibiotic Resistance

- Antibiotic resistance develops because of natural selection on a bacterial population.

B. Viruses

- Viruses can reproduce only inside host cells. They are composed of nucleic acids encased in a capsid and sometimes an envelope.

- Viruses cause disease by using host cell resources and by destroying host cells as part of the infectious cycle of the virus.

C. Eukaryotic Pathogens

D. Prions

- Infectious prions are comprised of protein only. They cause disease by refolding the host cell's naturally occurring prion proteins.

Key Terms: bacterium; binary fission; capsid; capsule; cell wall; contagious; flagellum; infectious; latent virus; microbe; nucleoid region; parasite; pathogen; pilus; plasmid; prion; prokaryote; viral envelope; virus

Instructor Resources in Teaching Toolbox: Chapter 12 PPT slides; TAs 206–212; 226–228; *Human Biology Animation: "Structure and Reproduction of Viruses"*

Figures and Tables:

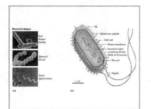

Figure 12.1
Bacterial Structure

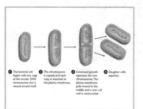

Figure 12.2
Binary Fission

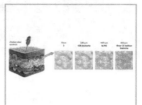

Figure 12.3
Exponential Growth of Bacteria

Table 12.1
Examples of Infectious
Diseases Caused by Bacteria

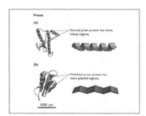

Figure 12.4
Viral Structure

Figure 12.5
Replication by an Enveloped
RNA Virus

Table 12.2
Examples of Infectious
Diseases Caused by Viruses

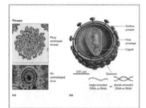

Figure 12.6
Prion Structure

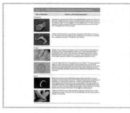

Table 12.3
Examples of Diseases Caused
by Eukaryotic Pathogens

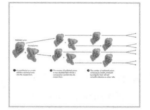

Figure 12.7
Replication by an Enveloped
RNA Virus

12.2 Transmission of Infectious Agents

A. Direct Contact

B. Indirect Contact

C. Vector-Borne Transmission

- An organism that carries disease-causing microbes from one host to another is called a vector.

D. Ingestion

Key Term: vector

Instructor Resources in Teaching Toolbox: Chapter 12 PPT slides; TA 213

Figures and Tables:

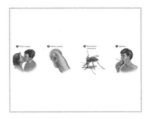

Figure 12.8
Transmission of Infectious Agents

12.3 The Body's Response to Infection: The Immune System

A. The First Line of Defense: Skin and Mucous Membranes

B. The Second Line of Defense: White Blood Cells, Inflammation, Defensive Proteins, and Fever

- White blood cells such as phagocytic macrophages and neutrophils engulf and digest foreign cells. Eosinophils bombard large invaders with digestive enzymes.

- Natural killer cells release chemicals that disintegrate cell membranes of tumor cells and virus-infected cells.

- Inflammation attracts phagocytes and promotes tissue healing.

C. The Third Line of Defense: Lymphocytes

- Lymphocytes help comprise the third, specific, line of defense in response to antigens on the surface of pathogens.

- Exposure to antigens causes increased production of B and T lymphocytes. B cells secrete antibodies against pathogens, and T cells attack invaders.

D. Anticipating Infection

E. Humoral and Cell-Mediated Immunity

F. There Is No Immune Response to Prions

Key Terms: active immunity; antibody; antigen; antigen receptor; antigen-presenting cells (APCs); autoimmune disease; B lymphocyte (B cell); basophil; cell-mediated immunity; clonal population; complement protein; cytotoxic T cell; eosinophil; fever; helper T cell; histamine; humoral immunity; immune response; inflammatory response; insulin-dependent diabetes; interferon; lupus; lymphocyte; macrophage; major histocompatibility complex (MHC) protein; mast cell; memory cell; multiple sclerosis; natural killer cell; neutrophil; nonspecific defense; passive immunity; phagocyte; plasma cell; pseudopodia; rheumatoid arthritis; specific defense; specificity; T lymphocyte (T cell); vaccination

Instructor Resources in Teaching Toolbox: Chapter 12 PPT slides; TAs 214–225, 229; *Human Biology Animations:* "The Inflammatory Response," "Antibody- and Cell-Mediated Immunity"; *BLAST! Tutorials:* "Inflammation," "Innate Immunity," "Adaptive Immunity"

Figures and Tables:

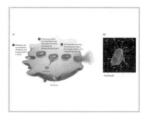

Figure 12.9
Phagocytosis

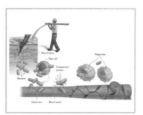

Figure 12.10
Inflammation

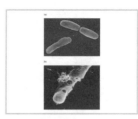

Figure 12.11
Complement Proteins

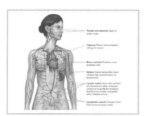

Figure 12.12
Lymphatic System

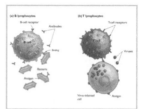

Figure 12.13
B Cells and T Cells

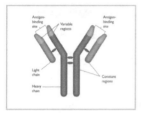

Figure 12.14
Antibody Structure

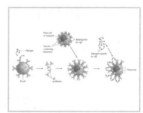

Figure 12.15
Allergy

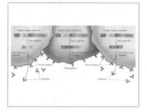

Figure 12.16
Genetic Rearrangements Allow
for the Production of Millions of
Different Antigen Receptors

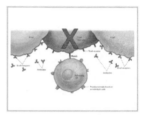

Figure 12.17
Testing Developing
Lymphocytes for Self-Proteins

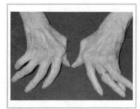

Figure 12.18
Autoimmune Disease

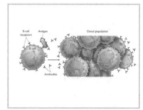

Figure 12.19
Humoral Immunity

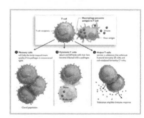

Figure 12.20
Cell-Mediated Immunity

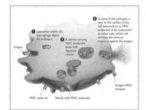

Figure 12.21
Antigen-Presenting Cell

Table 12.4
Cells of the Immune System

12.4   Preventing an Epidemic of Prion Diseases

- An epidemic is a contagious disease that spreads swiftly and widely among members of a population.

Key Terms: epidemic; epidemiologist

Instructor Resources in Teaching Toolbox: Chapter 12 PPT slides; *ABC News Video:* "Mad Cow"

In-Class Activity: Disease Outbreak Simulation: Bio-Rad produces a classroom kit—the ELISA Immuno Explorer Kit—that can be used to simulate disease outbreak and spread in the classroom (see Out of Class Activities section for more information). The exercise will take most of a class period, but students find it an entertaining learning experience.

Notes

Sexually Transmitted Infections: The Cervical Cancer Vaccine

13

Chapter at a Glance

13.1 The Old Epidemics

13.2 The New Epidemic—AIDS

Visual Lecture Outline

13.1 The Old Epidemics

- Sexually transmitted infections (STIs) are infections that are transferred via sexual contact.

A. The Eukaryotes: Pubic Lice and Trichomoniasis

B. The Bacteria: Chlamydia, Gonorrhea, and Syphilis

- All bacterial STIs can be cured with antibiotics, although some strains of gonorrhea are becoming resistant to multiple drugs.

C. The Viruses: Herpes, Hepatitis, and Genital Warts

- Infection with certain forms of human papillomavirus (HPV), the virus that causes genital warts, is associated with an increased risk of cervical cancer.

- Both hepatitis B and most cases of genital warts can be prevented by vaccination.

Key Terms: chlamydia; congenital syphilis; genital warts; gonorrhea; hepatitis; hepatitis B virus (HBV); herpes simplex; herpes simplex virus; human papillomavirus (HPV); pelvic inflammatory disease (PID); pubic lice; sexually transmitted disease (STD); sexually transmitted infection (STI); syphilis; trichomoniasis

Instructor Resources in Teaching Toolbox: Chapter 13 PPT slides; TAs 230–234, 239–240; *ABC News Video:* "Cervical Cancer Vaccine"

Figures and Tables:

Figure 13.1
Safer Sex, But Not Risk-Free

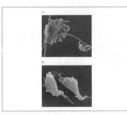

Figure 13.2
Infectious Insects and Protozoans

Table 13.1
STIs

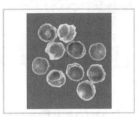

Figure 13.3
Bacterial STI

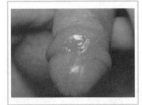

Figure 13.4
Primary Phase Syphilis

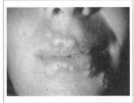

Figure 13.5
Herpes

Figure 13.6
Genital Warts

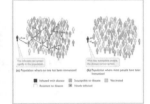

Figure 13.7
Disease Eradication

13.2 The New Epidemic—AIDS

A. A Disease of the Immune System

- HIV causes immune deficiency by killing helper T cells, resulting in individuals who cannot fight usually innocuous infections.

B. The Course of HIV Infection

- Although the body initially seems to control HIV infection, the virus continues to survive and evolve in the body. Eventually, in untreated individuals, the immune system loses control and the infection progresses to AIDS.

C. Treating HIV Infection

D. Preventing HIV/AIDS

- HIV infection is prevented by practicing abstinence, being engaged in a monogamous relationship with an uninfected partner, and using condoms during intercourse with someone whose HIV status is unknown.

Genes & Homeostasis: Resistance to HIV/AIDS

- CCR5 gene mutations confer resistance to HIV infection.

Key Terms: acquired immune deficiency syndrome (AIDS); asymptomatic; combination drug therapy; highly active retroviral therapy (HAART); HIV positive; human immunodeficiency virus (HIV); monogamous; opportunistic infections; retrovirus; reverse transcription

Instructor Resources in Teaching Toolbox: Chapter 13 PPT slides; TAs 235–238, 241; *Human Biology Animations:* "HIV: The AIDS Virus," "Effects of HIV on the Immune System"; *BLAST! Tutorials:* "HIV Structure," "AIDS Onset," "AIDS Treatment Strategies"; *ABC News Video:* "AIDS in South Africa"

In-Class Activity: Group Quiz: There are numerous online quizzes concerning AIDS and/or STDs (see the Out of Class Activities section for links). Use one of these quizzes or create your own in PowerPoint. Pose a question and get the class to participate in giving a consensus answer. This exercise can be used at the start of the lecture or at the end.

Figures and Tables:

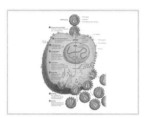

Figure 13.8

Reproductive Cycle of HIV

Figure 13.9

Evolution of HIV

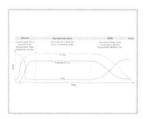

Figure 13.10

Typical Course of HIV Infection

Table 13.2

Anti-HIV Drugs

Figure 13.11

HIV Transmission

Notes

Brain Structure and Function: Attention Deficit Disorder

14

Chapter at a Glance

14.1 Nervous System Tissues
14.2 The Central Nervous System
14.3 The Limbic System and Memory
14.4 The Peripheral Nervous System
14.5 What Causes ADD?

Visual Lecture Outline

14.1 Nervous System Tissues

- The nervous system allows an organism to respond to external and internal stimuli.

- The nervous system consists of the brain and spinal cord of the central nervous system (CNS) as well as the nerves of the peripheral nervous system (PNS) that carry information to and from the CNS.

A. Neuron Structure

- Neuron structure consists of branching dendrites, a cell body, and an axon with terminal boutons.

B. The Creation of Nerve Impulses

C. Neurotransmitters Carry Signals Between Neurons

D. Neurotransmitters and Disease

Genes & Homeostasis: Is Depression Caused by Genes, the Environment, or Both?

E. Synaptic Integration

F. Neurotransmission, ADD, and Ritalin

Key Terms: acetylcholine; acetylcholinesterase; action potential; Alzheimer's disease; axon; cell body; central nervous system (CNS); dendrite; depolarization; depression; dopamine; effector; gray matter; integration; interneuron; motor neuron; myelin sheath; nerve; nerve impulse; nerve tract; nervous system; neuroglia; neuron; neurotransmitter; node of Ranvier; Parkinson's disease; peripheral nervous system (PNS); postsynaptic neuron; presynaptic neuron; refractory period; repolarization; resting potential; reuptake; Schwann cell; sensory neuron; sensory receptor; sodium-potassium pump; synapse; terminal bouton; white matter

Instructor Resources in Teaching Toolbox: Chapter 14 PPT slides; TAs 242–249, 259–261; *Human Biology Animations:* "Myelinated Neurons and Saltatory Conduction," "The Nerve Impulse," "The Synapse," "Psychoactive Drugs and the Brain"; *BioFlix:* "How Neurons Work," "Synapses"; *BLAST! Tutorials:* "Action Potential," "Signal Transmission at Synapses," "Cell Signaling: Neural," "Signal Amplifications in Neurons"

Figures and Tables:

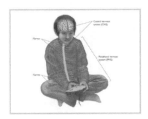

Figure 14.1
Central and Peripheral
Nervous Systems

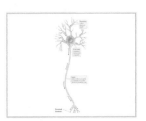

Figure 14.2
Structure of a Generalized
Neuron

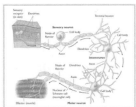

Figure 14.3
Types of Neurons

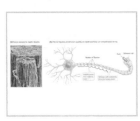

Figure 14.4
Myelination

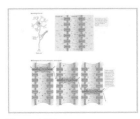

Figure 14.5
Generating and Propagating a
Nerve Impulse

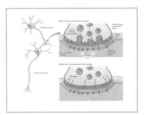

Figure 14.6
Transmitting the Nerve Impulse
Between Neurons

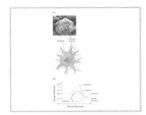

Figure 14.7
Integration

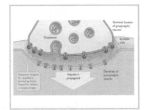

Figure 14.8
Mechanism of Ritalin Action

Table 14.1
Recreational Drugs and the
Nervous System

14.2   The Central Nervous System

- The spinal cord and brain are the two components of the CNS.

A. Spinal Cord

B. The Brain

C. ADD and the Structure and Function of the Brain

Key Terms: brain stem; caudate nuclei; cerebellum; cerebral cortex; cerebrospinal fluid; cerebrum; corpus callosum; fissure; frontal lobe; hypothalamus; medulla oblongata; meninges; midbrain; occipital lobe; parietal lobe; pons; reticular formation; spinal cord; spinal nerves; temporal lobe; thalamus; ventricles

Instructor Resources in Teaching Toolbox: Chapter 14 PPT slides; TAs 250–254; *ABC News Videos:* "Attention Deficit Hyperactivity Disorder," "Women and Alcohol"

In-Class Activity: The Stroop Test: Individuals with ADD often have difficulties with attention and impulsivity. The Stroop test is a commonly used diagnostic tool for identifying potential attention problems. It requires focus on a particular task while blocking out other features. A static version of the Stroop test, available at www.adhd.org.nz/stroop1.html, can be printed out in color and distributed to the class. It will only take a few minutes for the students to complete the activity. If computers are available to the students, a dynamic online version is available at www.dcity.org/braingames/stroop/. (A demonstration of the online version by the instructor can be great fun for the class as you demonstrate your difficulties with the tasks!)

Figures and Tables:

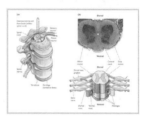

Figure 14.9
Spinal Cord and Nerves

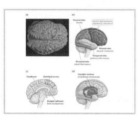

Figure 14.10
Structure of the Cerebrum

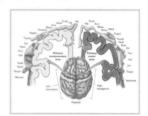

Figure 14.11
Cerebral Cortex

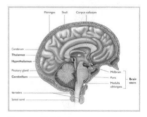

Figure 14.12
Anatomy of the Brain

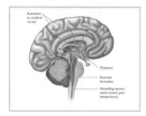

Figure 14.13
Reticular Formation

14.3 The Limbic System and Memory

- Control of emotional behavior, motivational drive, and the formation of some memories resides in the limbic system.

A. Limbic System Structures

- Structures in the limbic system are located near the base of the cerebrum and include the hippocampus and amygdala. The hippocampus is involved in memory and the amygdala in emotions.

B. Memory

Key Terms: amygdala; hippocampus; limbic system; memory

Instructor Resources in Teaching Toolbox: Chapter 14 PPT slides; TA 254

Figures and Tables:

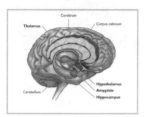

Figure 14.14
Limbic System

14.4 The Peripheral Nervous System

- The peripheral nervous system relays sensory and motor impulses between the CNS and the rest of the body.

A. The Nerves of the Peripheral Nervous System

B. Somatic System

C. The Autonomic Nervous System

Key Terms: autonomic nervous system; cranial nerve; ganglia; mixed nerve; parasympathetic division; peripheral nervous system; reflex; reflex arc; somatic system; sympathetic division

Instructor Resources in Teaching Toolbox: Chapter 14 PPT slides; TAs 255–258; *Human Biology Animations:* "Cranial and Spinal Nerves," "Reflex Arcs," "The Autonomic Nervous System"

Figures and Tables:

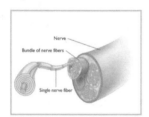

Figure 14.15
Nerves

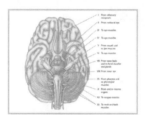

Figure 14.16
Cranial and Spinal Nerves

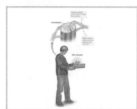

Figure 14.17
Reflex Arc

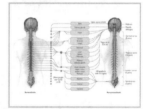

Figure 14.18
Autonomic Nervous System

14.5 What Causes ADD?

- There is no consensus about the cause or causes of ADD among members of the scientific community.

The Senses: Do Humans Have a Sixth Sense?

15

Chapter at a Glance

Visual Lecture Outline

15.1 Sensing and Perceiving

A. Sensory Receptors

- Sensory receptors can be defined by the type of input they receive: chemical (chemoreceptors), mechanical (mechanoreceptors), temperature (thermoreceptors), light (photoreceptors), or pain (nociceptors).

- Externoceptors sense conditions outside the body; internoceptors sense internal conditions.

B. Reading and Understanding the Environment

- Conscious perception of a stimulus can only occur when a stimulus is strong enough or important enough to send a signal to the brain's cortex.

- Sensory receptors can become adapted to stimuli over time, and their signals can drop below the point of perception.

Key Terms: chemoreceptor; depolarize; externoceptor; general sense; internoceptor; mechanoreceptors; nociceptor; pain receptor; perception; photoreceptor; sensation; sense organ; senses; sensory adaptation; sensory receptor; special sense; stimuli; thermoreceptor

Instructor Resources in Teaching Toolbox: Chapter 15 PPT slides; TAs 262–264, 292

In-Class Activity: Sensory Adaptation: Have students take a coin and place it on the back of their hand or forearm. Ask them to occasionally remember that coin on their skin while you continue with the lecture. At some point, they should experience sensory adaptation where they no longer perceive the coin against their skin.

Figures and Tables:

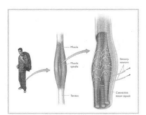

Table 15.1
Sensory Receptors

Figure 15.1
Variation in Sensory Capabilities

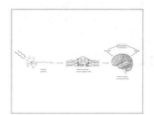

Figure 15.2
Steps of Information Processing

Figure 15.3
Is This Person a Threat?

15.2 The General Senses

A. Proprioception

B. The Sense of Touch

C. Temperature and Pain

Key Terms: chronic pain; fast pain; Golgi tendon organ; Meissner's corpuscle; Merkel disk; muscle spindle; Pacinian corpuscle; proprioceptor; receptive field; referred pain; Ruffini corpuscle; slow pain

Instructor Resources in Teaching Toolbox: Chapter 15 PPT slides; TAs 265–270

In-Class Activity: Proprioception: Instruct students to close their eyes. With their eyes closed, have them raise an arm parallel to the floor. Then have them bend the elbow of that arm, pointing their hand toward the ceiling. They should be visualizing their raised arm as making a 90-degree angle. Have them open their eyes and look at the arm. Their visualization should have been right on the money! It was their sense of proprioception that allowed them to know what that part of their body was doing in space without looking at it.

Figures and Tables:

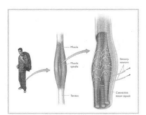

Figure 15.4
Muscle Spindle

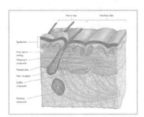

Figure 15.5
Touch Receptors

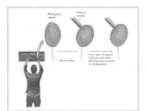

Figure 15.6
Touch Receptor Adaptation

Figure 15.7
Pain Chemical

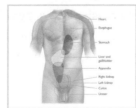

Figure 15.8
Referred Pain

Figure 15.9
High or Low Risk?

15.3 The Chemical Senses

    A. Taste

    B. Smell

Key Terms: gustatory receptor; odorant; olfactory bulb; olfactory receptor; papillae; pheromone; tastant; taste bud; taste cell; taste hair

Instructor Resources in Teaching Toolbox: Chapter 15 PPT slides; TAs 271–273

Figures and Tables:

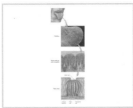
Figure 15.10
Taste

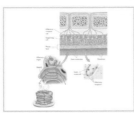
Figure 15.11
Smell

Figure 15.12
Smelling Cancer?

15.4 Senses of the Ear

    A. Hearing

    B. A Sense of Balance

Key Terms: auditory canal; auditory nerve; auditory receptor; basilar membrane; cochlea; cochlear duct; cochlear implant; cupula; ear; hair cell; ossicle; otolith organ; oval window; pinna; round window; saccule; semicircular canals; tectorial membrane; tympanic membrane; utricle; vertigo; vestibular apparatus

Instructor Resources in Teaching Toolbox: Chapter 15 PPT slides; TAs 274–282; *Human Biology Animation;* "The Human Ear"

Figures and Tables:

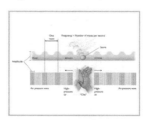

Figure 15.13
Sound Waves

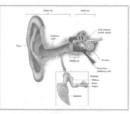

Figure 15.14
Pathway of Sound to the
Auditory Receptors

Figure 15.15
Auditory Receptors

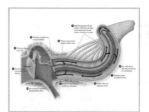

Figure 15.16
Function of the Cochlea

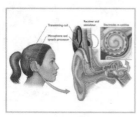

Figure 15.17
Cochlear Implant

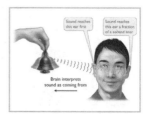

Figure 15.18
Triangulation

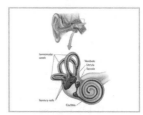

Figure 15.19
Vestibular Apparatus

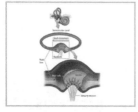

Figure 15.20
Sensing Head Movement

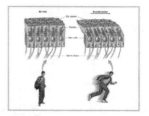

Figure 15.21
Sensing Gravity and Acceleration

15.5 Vision

- Vision is our primary sensory system.

A. Focusing Light

B. Photoreceptors

C. Vision and Perception

Genes & Homeostasis: Color Blindness

Key Terms: aqueous humor; astigmatism; bipolar cell; cataract; choroid; ciliary body; cones; cornea; eyes; fovea; ganglion cell; glaucoma; hyperopia; iris; lateral geniculate nucleus; lens; macular degeneration; myopia; optic chiasm; optic nerve; peripheral vision; photochemical; pupil; retina; retinal detachment; rhodopsin; rods; sclera; visible light; vitreous humor

Instructor Resources in Teaching Toolbox: Chapter 15 PPT slides; TAs 283–291; *Human Biology Animation:* "The Human Eye"; *ABC News Video:* "Allocation of Scarce Organs"

In-Class Activity: Fovea Centralis: Have students look at a distant wall. Tell them to concentrate their gaze on a wall feature, perhaps a clock. Although they are seeing the whole wall, the portion of the wall that they are concentrating on has its image focused onto the retinal fovea, the area of highest visual acuity. They did not have to consciously do this. The eye will position itself to project the image of attention onto the fovea.

Figures and Tables:

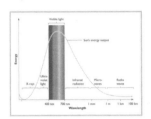

Figure 15.22
Makeup of Light

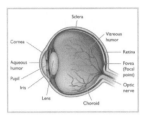

Figure 15.23
The Eye

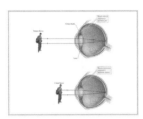

Figure 15.24
Focusing

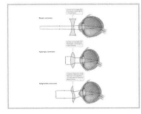

Figure 15.25
Improving Focus

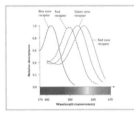

Figure 15.26
Color Vision

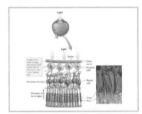

Figure 15.27
Signal Integration

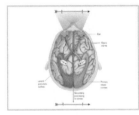

Figure 15.28
Visual Processing

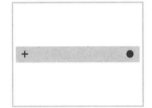

Figure 15.29
Blind Spot

Figure 15.30
Seeking Patterns

15.6 Predicting the Future

    A. Understanding Premonitions

    B. Expanding the Receptive Field

Instructor Resources in Teaching Toolbox: Chapter 15 PPT slides

Notes

The Endocrine System: Worried Sick

16

Chapter at a Glance

16.1 An Overview of the Endocrine System

16.2 The Endocrine System and Homeostasis

16.3 Other Endocrine Glands

16.4 Combating Stress

Visual Lecture Outline

16.1 An Overview of the Endocrine System

- The endocrine system is comprised of chemical messengers called hormones and the glands that secrete them.

A. Hormones: Chemical Messengers

- Hormones are chemicals that travel through the blood and elicit a response from specific cells and tissues.

B. Endocrine Glands

- Nine glands comprise the endocrine system: hypothalamus, pituitary, pineal, thyroid, parathyroid, thymus, adrenal, pancreas, and gonads.

C. Stress and the Endocrine System

Key Terms: adrenal gland; aldosterone; cortex; cortisol; cortisone; endocrine gland; epinephrine; glucocorticoid; hormone; medulla; mineralocorticoid; norepinephrine; protein hormone; receptor; secondary messenger; signal transduction; steroid hormone; stress response; target cell; target tissue

Instructor Resources in Teaching Toolbox: Chapter 16 PPT slides; TAs 293–296; *Human Biology Animation:* "How Hormones Influence Target Cells"; *BLAST! Tutorials:* "Cell Signaling: Endocrine," "Cell Signaling: Paracrine"; *ABC News Video:* "Fighting Stress"

Figures and Tables:

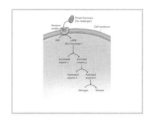

Figure 16.1
Protein Hormones and Signal Transduction

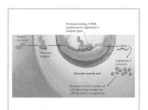

Figure 16.2
Steroid Hormone Function

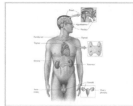

Figure 16.3
The Endocrine System

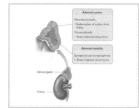

Figure 16.4
The Adrenal Gland

16.2 The Endocrine System and Homeostasis

A. The Control Center: The Hypothalamus

- The hypothalamus is a neuroendocrine organ that regulates many aspects of homeostasis and directs the stress response. It produces and releases hormones that affect the whole body as well as regulatory hormones that control the activities of the pituitary gland.

B. Turning Down Hormone Release Through Negative Feedback Loops

Key Terms: adrenocorticotropic hormone (ACTH); anterior pituitary; antidiuretic hormone (ADH); corticotrophin-releasing hormone (CRH); hypothalamus; hypothalamus-pituitary-adrenal axis; inhibiting hormone; oxytocin; pituitary gland; posterior pituitary; regulatory hormone; releasing hormone

Instructor Resources in Teaching Toolbox: Chapter 16 PPT slides; TAs 297–298; *Human Biology Animations:* "Hormonal Feedback Loops," "The Hypothalamus and Pituitary"; *BLAST! Tutorial:* "Cell Signaling via Steroid Hormones"

Figures and Tables:

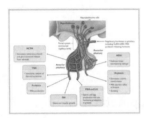

Figure 16.5
The Hypothalamus and Pituitary

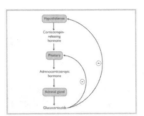

Figure 16.6
Negative Feedback in the Adrenals

16.3 Other Endocrine Glands

A. The Pituitary: Regulation of Growth

- The pituitary gland also releases growth hormone, which promotes the growth of muscle and bone, and prolactin, which triggers milk production and interferes with fertility.

Genes & Homeostasis: Size Matters

- Recombinant human growth hormone is available to treat individuals of short stature.

B. The Gonads: Sex-Specific Characteristics

C. The Pancreas: Regulating Blood Glucose Levels

- The pancreatic islets secrete glucagon and insulin, hormones that regulate blood sugar levels.

D. Thyroid and the Parathyroid: Metabolism and Development

- The thyroid and parathyroid glands work together to control blood calcium levels via release of the hormones calcitonin and parathyroid hormone.

E. The Pineal Gland: Hormonal Effects of Light and Darkness

F. The Thymus: Junction of the Endocrine and Immune Systems

G. Other Tissues That Produce Hormones

- Hormones are also produced by a number of organs whose main function is not endocrine in nature.

Key Terms: calcitonin; Cushing's syndrome; estrogen; follicle-stimulating hormone (FSH); gastrin; glucagon; gonad; gonadotropin-releasing hormone (GnRH); growth factor; growth hormone (GH); hyperthyroidism; hypothyroidism; insulin; leptin; luteinizing hormone (LH); melatonin; pancreatic islet; parathyroid gland; parathyroid hormone; pineal gland; progesterone; prolactin; prostaglandin; sex hormone; somatostatin; T3; T4; testosterone; thymopoietin; thymosin; thymus; thyroid gland

Instructor Resources in Teaching Toolbox: Chapter 16 PPT slides; TAs 299–308; 310–311

In-Class Activity: Endocrine Jeopardy: There are a lot of glands, hormones, target organs, and disorders to keep straight in this unit. An end-of-unit Jeopardy game is a fun learning tool. See Out of Class Activities section for links to Jeopardy templates.

Figures and Tables:

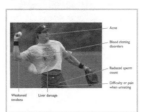

Figure 16.7
Steroid Abuse

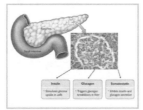

Figure 16.8
Pancreatic Islets

Figure 16.9
Cushing's Syndrome

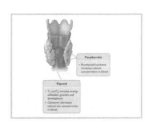

Figure 16.10
The Thyroid and Parathyroids

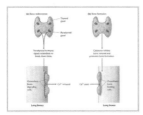

Figure 16.11
Calcium Regulation

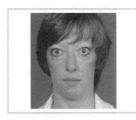

Figure 16.12
Graves' Disease

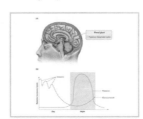

Figure 16.13
Daily Hormonal Cycles

Figure 16.14
Treatment for SAD

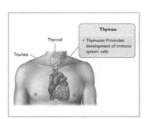

Figure 16.15
Thymus

Table 16.1
Endocrine Glands, their
Hormones, Targets, and Actions

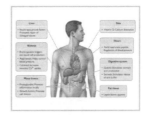

Figure 16.16
Other Endocrine Tissues

16.4 Combating Stress

- Although stress causes some disease, it also has value, preparing our bodies and minds for challenges.

Key Terms: Addison's disease

Instructor Resources in Teaching Toolbox: Chapter 16 PPT slides; TAs 309, 312

Figures and Tables:

Figure 16.17
Addison's Disease

Table 16.2
Techniques for Stress Relief

DNA Synthesis, Mitosis, and Meiosis: Cancer

17

Chapter at a Glance

Visual Lecture Outline

17.1 What Is Cancer?

- Unregulated cell division can lead to the formation of a tumor.

- Benign tumors are noncancerous tumors that do not grow and do not prevent surrounding organs from functioning.

- Malignant tumors are those that are invasive, or those that metastasize to surrounding tissues.

- Metastatic tumors move to other locations in the body, starting new cancers.

A. Risk Factors for Cancer

Key Terms: benign; cancer; carcinogen; cell division; malignant; metastasis; risk factor; tumor

Instructor Resources in Teaching Toolbox: Chapter 17 PPT slides; TAs 313–314; *Human Biology Animation: "Cancer"; ABC News Video: "Gene Therapy and Cancer"*

Figures and Tables:

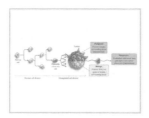

Figure 17.1
What Is Cancer?

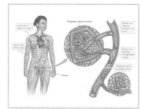

Figure 17.2
Metastasis

17.2 An Overview of Cell Division

A. DNA Replication

- Cell division is a process required for growth and development. For cell division to occur, the DNA must be copied and passed on to daughter cells.

Key Terms: centromere; chromosome; deoxyribonucleic acid (DNA); DNA polymerase; DNA replication; sister chromatid

Instructor Resources in Teaching Toolbox: Chapter 17 PPT slides; TAs 315–318; *Human Biology Animation:* "The Human Life Cycle"; *BioFlix:* "DNA Replication"

Figures and Tables:

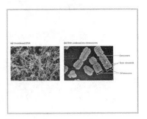

Figure 17.3
DNA Condenses During Cell Division

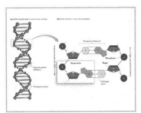

Figure 17.4
DNA Structure

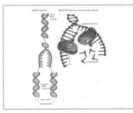

Figure 17.5
DNA Replication

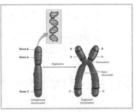

Figure 17.6
Unreplicated and Replicated Chromosomes

17.3 The Cell Cycle and Mitosis

- The cell cycle includes all events that occur as one cell gives rise to daughter cells.

A. Interphase: Normal Functioning and Preparations

B. Mitosis: The Nucleus Divides

C. Cytokinesis: The Cytoplasm Divides

Key Terms: anaphase; centriole; cytokinesis; interphase; metaphase; microtubule; mitosis; nuclear envelope; prophase; telophase

Instructor Resources in Teaching Toolbox: Chapter 17 PPT slides; TAs 319–322; *Human Biology Animation:* "Mitosis"; *BioFlix:* "Mitosis"

In-Class Activity: What Stage Am I In?: Mitosis is typically discussed by its classic stages (prophase, metaphase, anaphase, and telophase). Create a PowerPoint presentation of images of cells in the various stages of mitosis (acceptable images can be found in the teaching ancillaries that accompany this textbook and are also readily available on the Internet). Challenge the class to identify the correct mitotic stage of the cells shown. An additional approach is to list classic cellular events (e.g., separation of sister chromatids) and have the class identify the mitotic stage in which the listed event(s) occurs.

Figures and Tables:

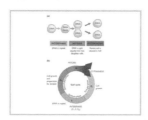

Figure 17.7
The Cell Cycle

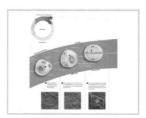

Figure 17.8a
Cell Division

Figure 17.8b (continued)

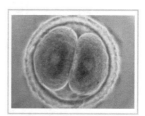

Figure 17.9
Cytokinesis

17.4 Mutations Override Cell Cycle Controls

A. Controls in the Cell Cycle

Genes & Homeostasis: Inheritance and Cancer

- Genes that encode the proteins regulating the cell cycle are called proto-oncogenes. When these normal genes become mutated, the genes are called oncogenes.

- Tumor suppressor genes are also involved in cancer. These genes encode proteins that suppress or stop cell division if conditions are not favorable. Mutant tumor suppressors allow cells to override cell cycle checkpoints.

Key Terms: anchorage dependence; angiogenesis; contact inhibition; growth factor; immortal; oncogenes; proto-oncogenes; telomerase; tumor suppressors

Instructor Resources in Teaching Toolbox: Chapter 17 PPT slides; TA 322

Figures and Tables:

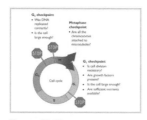

Figure 17.10
Controls of the Cell Cycle

17.5 Cancer Detection and Treatment

A. Detecting Cancer

- A biopsy is a common method for detecting cancer.

B. Cancer Treatments: Chemotherapy and Radiation

- Typical cancer treatments include chemotherapy, which involves injecting chemicals that kill rapidly dividing cells, and radiation, which involves killing tumor cells by exposing them to high-energy particles.

Key Terms: biopsy; chemotherapy; laparoscope; radiation therapy; remission

Instructor Resources in Teaching Toolbox: Chapter 17 PPT slides; TAs 323–324

Figures and Tables:

Figure 17.11
Warning Signs of Cancer

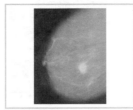

Figure 17.12
Mammography

Figure 17.13
Chemotherapy

17.6 Meiosis: Making Reproductive Cells

- Meiosis is a type of cell division that gives rise to gametes.
- Gametes contain half as many chromosomes as do somatic cells.

A. Interphase

B. Meiosis I

C. Meiosis II

D. Crossing Over and Random Alignment

Key Terms: allele; autosome; crossing over; diploid (2*n*); gamete; haploid (*n*); homologous pair; karyotype; linked genes; meiosis; random alignment; sex chromosome; somatic; zygote

Instructor Resources in Teaching Toolbox: Chapter 17 PPT slides; TAs 325–334; *Human Biology Animations:* "Meiosis," "Comparing Mitosis and Meiosis"; *BioFlix:* "Meiosis"

In-Class Activity: Mitosis and Meiosis Video: Learning the events of mitosis and meiosis are well suited to video presentation. A good video, *Mitosis and Meiosis* (Cat. No. 782615), can be obtained from Discovery Education at http://teacherstore.discovery.com/.

Figures and Tables:

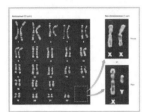

Figure 17.14
Karyotype

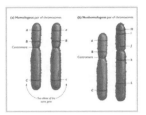

Figure 17.15
Homologous and
Nonhomologous Pairs of
Chromosomes

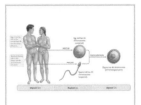

Figure 17.16
Gamete Production

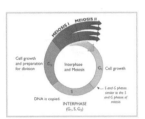

Figure 17.17
Interphase and Meiosis

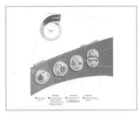

Figure 17.18a
The Cell Cycle

Figure 17.18b (continued)

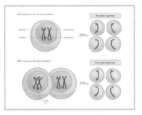

Figure 17.19
Crossing Over

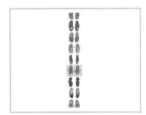

Figure 17.20
Random Alignment: An Analogy
Using Shoes

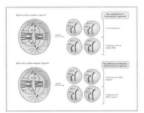

Figure 17.21
Random Alignment of
Chromosomes

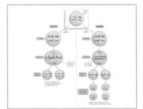

Figure 17.22
Comparing Mitosis and Meiosis

Notes

Human Reproduction: Fertility and Infertility

18

Chapter at a Glance

18.1 The Human Reproductive Systems
18.2 Gametogenesis: Development of Sex Cells
18.3 The Menstrual Cycle
18.4 The Human Sexual Response
18.5 Controlling Fertility
18.6 Health, Lifestyle, and Fertility

Visual Lecture Outline

18.1 The Human Reproductive Systems

- Sexual reproduction requires a mating between two parents. Males and females produce gametes in structures called gonads. Gametes unite at fertilization to produce genetically distinct offspring.

A. The Male Reproductive System

B. The Female Reproductive System

Key Terms: androgen; bulbourethral gland; cervix; clitoris; endometrium; epididymis; fimbria; gamete; glans penis; gonad; labia majora; labia minora; Leydig cell; ovary; oviduct; penis; prostate gland; scrotum; semen; seminal vesicle; seminiferous tubule; sexual reproduction; testis (plural, testes); urethra; uterus; vagina; vas deferens; vulva

Instructor Resources in Teaching Toolbox: Chapter 18 PPT slides; TAs 335–336; *Human Biology Animations:* "The Male Reproductive System," "The Female Reproductive System"

Figures and Tables:

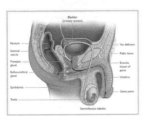

Figure 18.1
Male Reproductive Anatomy

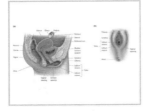

Figure 18.2
Female Reproductive Anatomy

18.2 Gametogenesis: Development of Sex Cells

A. Spermatogenesis: Development of Men's Gametes

- Spermatogenesis occurs in the seminiferous tubules of the testes and begins at puberty.

B. Oogenesis: The Development of Women's Gametes

- Oogenesis occurs in the ovaries and results in the production of egg cells. This process begins while the female is still in her mother's uterus and then pauses until puberty.

Genes & Homeostasis: Endocrine Disruptors

Key Terms: acrosome; corpus luteum; embryo; follicle; follicle-stimulating hormone (FSH); gametogenesis; gonadotropin-releasing hormone (GnRH); luteinizing hormone (LH); oogenesis; ovarian cycle; ovulation; polar body; Sertoli cell; sperm; spermatogenesis; testosterone

Instructor Resources in Teaching Toolbox: Chapter 18 PPT slides; TAs 337–346

Figures and Tables:

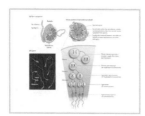

Figure 18.3
Spermatogenesis

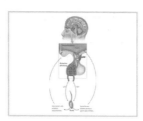

Figure 18.4
Hormonal Control of the Testes

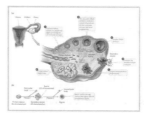

Figure 18.5
Oogenesis

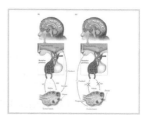

Figure 18.6
Hormonal Control of the Ovaries

18.3 The Menstrual Cycle

- High levels of estrogen cause increased FSH and LH production. High levels of progesterone cause decreased FSH and LH secretion.

Key Terms: endometriosis; menstrual cycle

Instructor Resources in Teaching Toolbox: Chapter 18 PPT slides; TA 347; *Human Biology Animation:* "Preparation of the Endometrium for Implantation"

Figures and Tables:

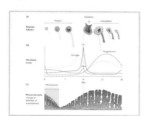

Figure 18.7
Menstrual Cycle

18.4 The Human Sexual Response

- The physiology of human sexuality is typically described as a four-stage process: excitement, which prepares the body for intercourse; plateau, where sexual tension builds; orgasm, the release of that tension; and resolution, a return to baseline conditions.

Key Terms: four-stage model; orgasm

Instructor Resources in Teaching Toolbox: Chapter 18 PPT slides; TA 348

Figures and Tables:

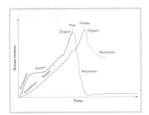

Figure 18.8
Human Sexual Response Cycle

18.5 Controlling Fertility

- Unintended pregnancy can be prevented by the use of contraception, that is, methods that interfere with the process of human reproduction.

A. Principles of Fertility Control

B. Barrier Methods

C. Hormonal Birth Control

D. Other Methods of Birth Control

E. The Future of Birth Control Technology

Key Terms: barrier method; calendar method; cervical cap; combined hormone contraceptive; condom; contraception; contraceptive patch; contraceptive sponge; diaphragm; elective abortion; emergency contraception; female latex condom; fertility awareness method; intrauterine device (IUD); mifepristone; oral contraceptive; progesterone-only pill; spermicide; symptothermal method; tubal ligation; vacuum aspiration; vaginal ring; vasectomy; withdrawal

Instructor Resources in Teaching Toolbox: Chapter 18 PPT slides; TAs 349–358; *Human Biology Animation:* "Ovulation and Hormonal Birth Control Methods"

In-Class Activity: Birth Control Methods: Pictures and descriptions are fine, but nothing can substitute for holding the real thing in your hand. Planned Parenthood organizations have educational kits available. Two popular kits are the Birth Control Resource Kit, which can be ordered from www.plannedparenthood.org/westernwashington/birth-control-resource-kit.htm, and the Contraceptive Methods Demonstration Kit, which can be obtained from www.plannedparenthood.org/ma/materials-and-resources.htm. The kit contains actual examples and fact sheets for the most popular current contraceptive methods. Pass around the articles while you discuss the topic of fertility control. If your teaching situation allows, you could also display the kit contents during a lab session or at some other time that would allow students to examine the materials at a more leisurely pace.

Figures and Tables:

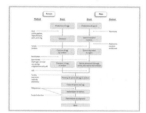

Figure 18.9
Birth Control and Human Reproduction

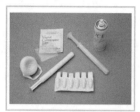

Figure 18.10
Spermicides

Table 18.1
Effectiveness of Birth Control Methods

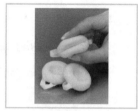

Figure 18.11
Contraceptive Sponge

Figure 18.12
Condoms

Figure 18.13
Barriers to the Cervix

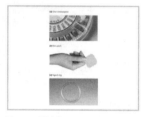

Figure 18.14
Hormonal Contraceptives

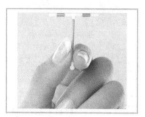

Figure 18.15
Intrauterine Devices

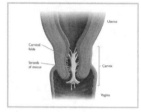

Figure 18.16
Fertility and Mucus

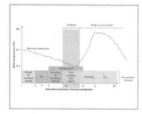

Figure 18.17
Fertility Awareness

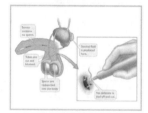

Figure 18.18
Vasectomy

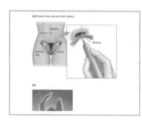

Figure 18.19
Female Sterilization

Figure 18.20
A Divisive Issue

18.6 Health, Lifestyle, and Fertility

Instructor Resources in Teaching Toolbox: *ABC News Video:* "Gender Selection"

Heredity: Genes and Intelligence

19

Chapter at a Glance

19.1 The Inheritance of Traits

19.2 Mendelian Genetics: When the Role of a Gene Is Direct

19.3 Quantitative Genetics: When Genes and Environment Interact

19.4 Genes, the Environment, and the Individual

Visual Lecture Outline

19.1 The Inheritance of Traits

A. Genes and Chromosomes

- All cells in a body have the same genes, but the timing of expression and the combination of these genes determines the activities of a particular cell.

B. Producing Diversity in Offspring

- Mutations in gene copies can cause slightly different proteins to be produced within cells. Different gene versions are called alleles.

Key Terms: genetic variation; independent assortment; random fertilization; segregation

Instructor Resources in Teaching Toolbox: Chapter 19 PPT slides; TAs 359–362; *Human Biology Animation:* "Sex-Linked Traits"; *BLAST! Tutorials:* "Genetic Variation: Independent Assortment," "Fusion of Gametes"

Figures and Tables:

Figure 19.1
Genes as Words in an Instruction Manual

Figure 19.2
The Formation of Different Alleles

Figure 19.3
Two Complete Instruction Manuals

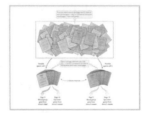

Figure 19.4
Each Egg and Each Sperm Is Unique

19.2 Mendelian Genetics: When the Role of a Gene Is Direct

A. Genotype and Phenotype

- The phenotype of a given individual for a particular gene depends on which alleles the individual carries (its genotype) and whether the alleles are dominant or recessive.

B. Genetic Diseases in Human Beings

C. Using Punnett Squares to Predict Genotypes of Offspring

- A Punnett square helps us determine the probability that two parents of known genotype will produce a child with a particular genotype.

Key Terms: cross; dominant; genotype; heterozygous; homozygous; phenotype; Punnett square; recessive

Instructor Resources in Teaching Toolbox: Chapter 19 PPT slides; TAs 363–366; *Human Biology Animations:* "Codominance and Incomplete Dominance," "One- and Two-Trait Crosses"; *BLAST! Tutorials:* "Single-Trait Crosses," "Two-Trait Crosses"

In-Class Activity: What Is Your Phenotype?: Students love assessing their own genetic makeup for simple Mendelian traits. Have the class assess whether they possess the dominant or the recessive phenotype for the following 10 traits: *Ear lobes:* The allele for free earlobes (F) is dominant to the allele for attached earlobes (f). An individual with free earlobes will be either homozygous dominant (FF) or heterozygous (Ff). An individual with attached earlobes will be homozygous for the recessive allele (ff). *Hairline:* Widow's peak is dominant to straight hairline. *Little finger:* A little finger that bends slightly toward the fourth finger shows the dominant phenotype. A straight little finger is the recessive phenotype. *Interlacing fingers:* When folding the two hands together, left thumb on top is dominant to right thumb on top. *Freckles:* The presence of freckles is dominant to the no freckle state. *Tongue rolling:* The ability to roll the tongue into a cylindrical shape is dominant to the inability to do so. *Hitchhiker's thumb:* If the last joint of the thumb can be bent back at an angle of 60 degrees or more this is the recessive phenotype. The inability to bend the thumb in such a manner is dominant. *Dimpled/cleft chin:* The allele for dimpled chin is dominant to the nondimpled allele. *Mid-digital hair:* The allele for hair on the middle segment of the finger is dominant to the no mid-digital hair allele. *Extra digits:* The allele for polydactyly (extra fingers or toes) is dominant to the nonpolydactyl allele. Collect and tabulate the class results. Share the results with the class. Many students will initially believe that dominant traits would always be more common in the population than recessive traits. Show them that this is not the case by looking at the class data.

Figures and Tables:

Figure 19.5
Gregor Mendel

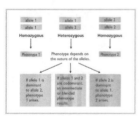

Figure 19.6
Genotypes and Phenotypes

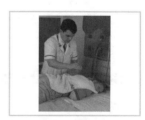

Figure 19.7
Treating Cystic Fibrosis

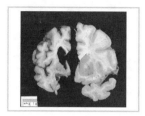

Figure 19.8

Effects of Huntington's Allele

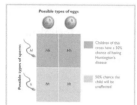

Figure 19.9

Calculating the Risk of Cystic Fibrosis

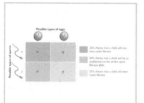

Figure 19.10

Calculating the Likelihood of a Dominant Disease

19.3 Quantitative Genetics: When Genes and Environment Interact

- Many traits—such as height, IQ, and musical ability—show quantitative variation, which results in a range of values for the trait within a given population.

A. Why Traits Are Quantitative

B. The Heritability of Quantitative Traits

Key Terms: continuous variation; heritability; natural experiments; polygenic traits; quantitative traits

Instructor Resources in Teaching Toolbox: Chapter 19 PPT slides; TAs 367–369, 372

Figures and Tables:

Figure 19.11

A Bell Curve

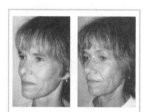

Figure 19.12

The Effect of the Environment on Phenotype

Figure 19.13

Skin Color Is Influenced by Genes and Environment

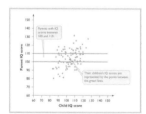

Figure 19.14

Correlation Between Parents and Children

Table 19.1

To What Extent Is IQ Heritable?

19.4 Genes, the Environment, and the Individual

A. The Use and Misuse of Heritability Calculations

B. How Do Genes Matter?

Instructor Resources in Teaching Toolbox: Chapter 19 PPT slides; TAs 370–371

Figures and Tables:

Figure 19.15
The Environment Can Have
Powerful Effects on Highly
Heritable Traits

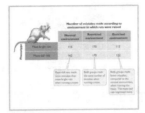

Figure 19.16
A Highly Heritable Trait Is Not
Identical in All Environments

Complex Patterns of Inheritance: DNA Detective

Chapter at a Glance

Visual Lecture Outline

20.1 Extensions of Mendelism

- Some traits are not inherited in the straightforward manner described by Mendel.

- Polygenic inheritance occurs when many genes control one trait.

- Incomplete dominance is an extension of Mendelian genetics whereby the phenotype of the progeny is intermediate to that of both parents.

- Codominance occurs when both alleles of a given gene are expressed.

Key Terms: codominance; hemophilia; incomplete dominance; multiple allelism; pleiotropy

Instructor Resources in Teaching Toolbox: Chapter 20 PPT slides; TAs 373–374, 386

Figures and Tables:

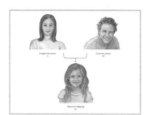

Figure 20.1
Incomplete Dominance

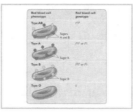

Figure 20.2
Red Blood Cell Phenotypes and Genotypes

Table 20.1
Percentages of Blood Types in the U.S. Population

20.2 Dihybrid Crosses

- Dihybrids are heterozygous for two traits. It is possible to predict the outcome of a dihybrid cross by using a Punnett square.

Key Term: phenotypic ratio

Instructor Resources in Teaching Toolbox: Chapter 20 PPT slides; TAs 375–376

Figures and Tables:

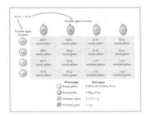

Figure 20.3
Dihybrid Cross

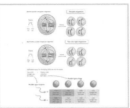

Figure 20.4
Random Alignment of
Chromosomes Leads to
Independent Assortment of
Genes

20.3 Sex Determination and Sex Linkage

A. Chromosomes and Sex Determination

- Males have both an X and a Y chromosome and can produce gametes containing either sex chromosome. Females have two X chromosomes and always produce gametes containing an X chromosome.

B. Sex Linkage

Genes & Homeostasis: Changes to Chromosome Structure and Number

- The failure of chromosomes to separate during meiosis is called nondisjunction. The presence of an extra chromosome is known as trisomy. The absence of one chromosome of a homologous pair is called monosomy.

Key Terms: autosome; carrier; sex chromosome; sex determination; sex-linked gene; X-linked gene; Y-linked gene

Instructor Resources in Teaching Toolbox: Chapter 20 PPT slides; TAs 377–378

Figures and Tables:

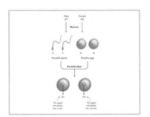

Figure 20.5
Sex Determination in Humans

Figure 20.6
X and Y Chromosomes

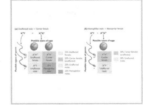

Figure 20.7
Genetic Crosses Involving the
X-Linked Hemophilia Trait

20.4 Pedigrees

- Pedigrees are charts that scientists use to study the transmission of genetic traits among related individuals.

Key Term: pedigree

Instructor Resources in Teaching Toolbox: Chapter 20 PPT slides; TAs 379–381

Figures and Tables:

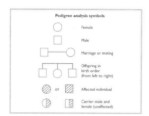

Figure 20.8
Pedigree Analysis

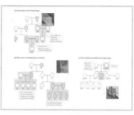

Figure 20.9
Pedigrees Showing Different
Modes of Inheritance

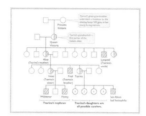

Figure 20.10
Origin and Inheritance of the
Hemophilia Allele

20.5 DNA Fingerprinting

- DNA fingerprinting is a technique used to connect individuals to DNA evidence and to show the relatedness of individuals based on similarities in their DNA sequences.

A. Copying DNA Through Polymerase Chain Reaction

B. Size-Based Separation Through Gel Electrophoresis

Key Terms: agarose gel; denatured; DNA fingerprinting; gel electrophoresis; polymerase chain reaction (PCR); *Taq* polymerase

Instructor Resources in Teaching Toolbox: Chapter 20 PPT slides; TAs 382–385, 387; *BLAST! Tutorials:* "DNA Fingerprinting," "Gel Electrophoresis"

In-Class Activity: Gel Electrophoresis: This activity requires the availability of the correct equipment and sufficient time to carry out the procedure. It is an excellent activity for a lab session but can be made to fit into a more traditional lecture setting or presented in part as a teacher demonstration. Bio-Rad (www.bio-rad.com) offers an excellent kit, "Analysis of Pre-cut Lambda DNA," which teaches separation of DNA fragments on an agarose gel.

In-Class Activity: DNA Forensics: The popularity of television crime dramas and paperback mystery novels is a testament to our love of a good mystery. Your class will enjoy using DNA forensics to solve simple problems you can create for them. Some nice hypothetical cases can be obtained from the Internet and incorporated into a fun activity. Two possibilities are listed to get you started.

- A DNA fingerprinting worksheet that asks student to evaluate a hypothetical paternity case is available at www.pbs.org/wgbh/aso/resources/guide/earthappenact3.html.

- The Biology Project is a DNA Forensics Problem Set with crime and paternity problems that can be copied and distributed to the class for them to solve. It is available at www.biology.arizona.edu/human_bio/problem_sets/DNA_forensics_2 /DNA_forensics.html.

Figures and Tables:

Figure 20.11
PCR

Figure 20.12
Gel Electrophoresis

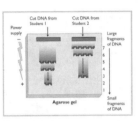

Figure 20.13
DNA Fingerprint

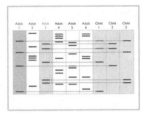

Figure 20.14
Hypothetical Fingerprint of Adult and Child Skeletons

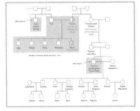

Figure 20.15
Anna Anderson

Figure 20.16
Romanov Family Pedigree

Table 20.2
The Scientific Method

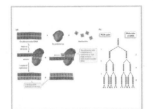

Figure 20.17
Funeral for the Romanovs

Development and Aging: The Promise and Perils of Stem Cells

21

Chapter at a Glance

Visual Lecture Outline

21.1 The Production of Embryonic Stem Cells

A. Fertilization: Forming the Ultimate Stem Cell

B. Preembryonic Development

Key Terms: blastocyst; capacitation; cell differentiation; cleavage; conjoined twins; development; dizygotic twins; embryo; embryonic stem cells; extraembryonic membranes; fertilization; fetal stem cells; fetus; in vitro fertilization (IVF); inner cell mass; monozygotic twins; morphogenesis; multipotent; ovum; pluripotent; preembryo; regenerative medicine; stem cell; totipotent; trophoblast; zona pellucida; zygote

Instructor Resources in Teaching Toolbox: Chapter 21 PPT slides; TAs 388–391, 403; *Human Biology Animation:* "Embryonic Development"; *ABC News Videos:* "Stem Cell Breakthrough," "Human Stem Cells"

Figures and Tables:

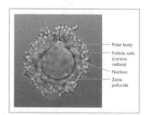

Figure 21.1
Human Egg Cell Before Fertilization

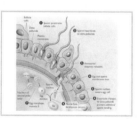

Figure 21.2
Fertilization

Figure 21.3
Development of the Early Embryo

Table 21.1
Extraembryonic Membranes

21.2 Early Embryonic Development

Key Terms: amnion; amniotic fluid; clinical pregnancy; ectoderm; ectopic pregnancy; embryonic disk; endoderm; gastrula; human chorionic gonadotropin (HCG); implantation; mesoderm; miscarriage; yolk sac

Instructor Resources in Teaching Toolbox: Chapter 21 PPT slides; TAs 392–393

Figures and Tables:

Figure 21.4
Implantation

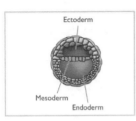

Figure 21.5
Gastrulation

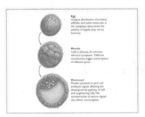

Figure 21.6
The Process of Cell Differentiation

21.3 Organ Formation

A. Cell Migration and Death

B. Early Organogenesis: Development of the Nervous System

C. Later Organogenesis: The Reproductive Organs

Key Terms: apoptosis; cell migration; genital tubercle; indifferent gonads; labioscrotal swellings; Müllerian duct; neural tube; organogenesis; spina bifida; *SRY* gene; Wolffian duct

Instructor Resources in Teaching Toolbox: Chapter 21 PPT slides; TAs 394–396, 404

Figures and Tables:

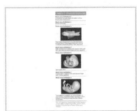

Table 21.2
Embryonic Development

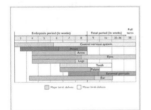

Figure 21.7
Organ System Development

Figure 21.8
Formation of the Neural Tube

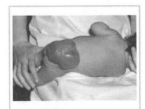

Figure 21.9
Neural Tube Defects

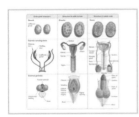

Figure 21.10
Determination of Sex of Reproductive Organs

21.4 Fetal Development and Birth

A. The Purpose of the Placenta in Pregnancy

B. Fetal Circulation

C. Stem Cells and the Fetal Period

D. The Process of Childbirth

Key Terms: amniocentesis; breech; Caesarean section; chorionic villi; ductus arteriosus; ductus venosus; foramen ovale; labor; parturition; placenta; prolactin; somatomammotropin; ultrasound; umbilical cord

Instructor Resources in Teaching Toolbox: Chapter 21 PPT slides; TAs 397–401, 405

In-Class Activity: Birth: Watching the birth of a baby or the development of a fetus can make quite a visual impact. Numerous videos are available for purchase. You could also view the *NOVA* program on reproduction and development (*Life's Greatest Miracle*) online at www.pbs.org/wgbh/nova/miracle/program.html. The hour-long program is divided into eight chapters that can be viewed individually.

Figures and Tables:

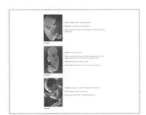

Figure 21.11
Fetal Development

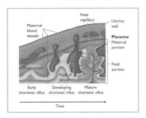

Figure 21.12
Chorionic Villi

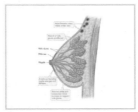

Figure 21.13
Breast Development During Pregnancy

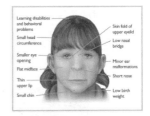

Figure 21.14
Fetal Alcohol Syndrome

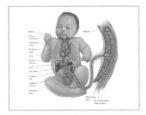

Figure 21.15
Fetal Circulation

Table 21.3
Screening Tests Used During Pregnancy

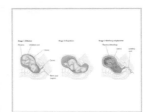

Figure 21.16
The Three Stages of Labor

21.5 Development After Birth

A. Growth and Maturation

B. Puberty

Genes & Homeostasis: Are Girls Becoming Women Too Young?

Key Terms: adolescence; adulthood; allometric growth; childhood; infancy; lactation; menarche; neonatal; pubescence; secondary sex characteristics

Instructor Resources in Teaching Toolbox: Chapter 21 PPT slides; TA 402

Figures and Tables:

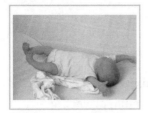

Figure 21.17
Nervous System After Birth

Figure 21.18
Lactation

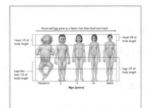

Figure 21.19
Allometric Growth

21.6 Aging

A. Why Do We Age?

B. Effects of Aging

C. Restoring the Brain

Key Terms: gerontology; Parkinson's disease (PD); senescence; telomeres

Instructor Resources in Teaching Toolbox: Chapter 21 PPT slides; TA 402; *ABC News Video:* "Caring for Elderly Parents"

Figures and Tables:

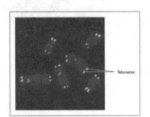

Figure 21.20
Telomeres

Figure 21.21
Premature Aging

Evolution: Where Did We Come From?

Chapter at a Glance

Visual Lecture Outline

22.1 Evidence of Evolution

    A. What Is Evolution?

    B. Charles Darwin's Revolution

    C. Alternative Hypotheses: Scientific and Religious

    D. Evidence from Biological Classification

    E. Evidence from Homology: Related Species Are Similar

    F. Evidence from Biogeography

    G. Evidence from the Fossil Record

Key Terms: biogeography; biological evolution; classification systems; fossils; hominin; homology; radiometric dating; species; theory of common descent; theory of evolution; vestigial traits

Instructor Resources in Teaching Toolbox: Chapter 22 PPT slides; TAs 406–414, 420; *Human Biology Animations:* "Principles of Evolution," "Biogeography and Continental Movement," "Agents of Change"; *BLAST! Tutorial:* "Evidence for Evolution: Homologous Limbs"

Figures and Tables:

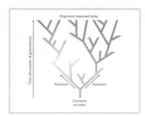

Figure 22.1
The Theory of Common Descent

Figure 22.2
Charles Darwin

Figure 22.3
Giant Tortoises of the Galápagos

Table 22.1
Classification of Life

Figure 22.4
Homology of Mammal Forelimbs

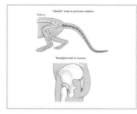

Figure 22.5
Vestigial Traits Reflect Our Evolutionary Heritage

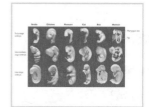

Figure 22.6
Similarity Among Chordate Embryos

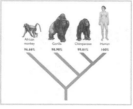

Figure 22.7
Similar Organisms Have Similar DNA Sequences

Figure 22.8
Fossilization

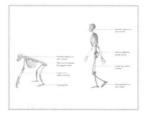

Figure 22.9
Anatomical Differences Among Humans and Chimpanzees

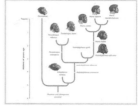

Figure 22.10
Evolutionary Relationships Among Hominin Species

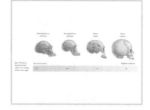

Figure 22.11
Ape-to-Human Transition

22.2 The Origin of Species

    A. Speciation: How One Becomes Two

    B. The Theory of Natural Selection

    C. Critical Thinking About Natural Selection

    D. Evolution: A Robust Theory

Key Terms: adaptation; biological species concept; diverge; fitness; populations; reproductive isolation; speciation; theory of natural selection

Instructor Resources in Teaching Toolbox: Chapter 22 PPT slides; TAs 415–418; *BLAST! Tutorials:* "Natural Selection"

Figures and Tables:

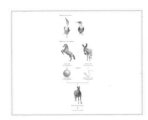

Figure 22.12
Reproductive Isolation

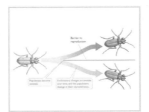

Figure 22.13
Isolation of Population Leads
to Divergence of Traits

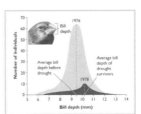

Figure 22.14
Survival and Reproduction Are
Not Random

Figure 22.15
The Panda's Thumb

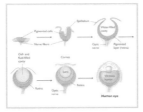

Figure 22.16
Eye Evolution

22.3 Human Evolution

A. Why Human Groups Differ: Selection and Genetic Drift

B. Evolution in the Classroom

Key Terms: assortative mating; founder effect; genetic drift; population bottleneck; sexual selection

Instructor Resources in Teaching Toolbox: Chapter 22 PPT slides; TA 419; *ABC News Video:* "Culture Wars: Evolution"

In-Class Activity: Becoming Human: The Institute of Human Origins has an excellent presentation titled *Becoming Human* that is narrated by famed paleoanthropologist Donald Johanson (www.becominghuman.org/). This presentation serves as a good introduction to class discussion of human evolution.

Figures and Tables:

Figure 22.17
Linnaean Classification of
Human Variety

Figure 22.18
Relationships Between UV
Light Levels, Folate, Vitamin D,
and Skin Color

Figure 22.19
Effects of Sexual Selection

Notes

Ecology: Is Earth Experiencing a Mass Extinction?

Chapter at a Glance

23.1 Limits to Population Growth

23.2 The Sixth Extinction

23.3 Saving Species

Visual Lecture Outline

23.1 Limits to Population Growth

A. Principles of Population Ecology

B. Population Crashes

Key Terms: carrying capacity; density-dependent factor; density-independent factor; ecology; exponential growth; logistic growth; population; population crash; population pyramid

Instructor Resources in Teaching Toolbox: Chapter 23 PPT slides; TAs 421–423

Figures and Tables:

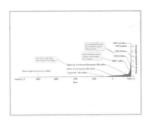

Figure 23.1
Human Population Growth

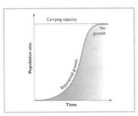

Figure 23.2
Logistic Growth Curve

Figure 23.3
Crash of Human Population

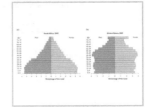

Figure 23.4
Time Lag in Human Population Growth

23.2 The Sixth Extinction

A. Measuring Extinction Rates

B. Causes of Extinction

C. The Consequences of Extinction

Key Terms: biodiversity; biomass; community; competition; consumer; decomposer; ecosystem; Endangered Species Act (ESA); extinction; food chain; food web; habitat; habitat destruction; habitat fragmentation; introduced species; keystone species; mass extinction; mutualism; nutrient cycling; overexploitation; predation; producer; species-area curve; trophic level

Instructor Resources in Teaching Toolbox: Chapter 23 PPT slides; TAs 424–427, 429; *Human Biology Animations:* "Energy Flow and Food Webs," "The Water Cycle," "The Carbon Cycle," "The Nitrogen Cycle"; *BLAST! Tutorials:* "Energy Flow," "Carbon Cycle," "Nitrogen Cycle"

Figures and Tables:

Figure 23.5
Rate of Extinction

Figure 23.6
Lost Species

Figure 23.7
Predicting Extinction Caused
by Habitat Destruction

Figure 23.8
Trophic Pyramid

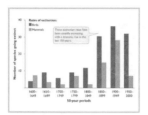

Figure 23.9
Web of Life

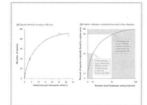

Figure 23.10
Keystone Species

Table 23.1
Type of Species Interactions
and Their Direct Effects

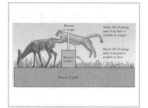

Figure 23.11
Nutrient Cycling

23.3   Saving Species

A. Protecting Habitat

B. Ensuring Adequate Population Size

C. Meeting the Needs of Humans and Nature

Key Term: restoration ecology

Instructor Resources in Teaching Toolbox: Chapter 23 PPT slides; TA 428, 430; *ABC News Video:* "Bird Flu"

In-Class Activity: Ecology Videos: The Annenberg Foundation has several very good 30-minute videos that would be appropriate to topics in this chapter (ecosystems, human population dynamics, biodiversity loss, etc.). The series, *The Habitable Planet*, at www.learner.org/resources/series209.html is excellent. The videos can be ordered or viewed online.

In-Class Activity: Guest Lecturers: Community outreach and education are important to environmental organizations and government agencies. Invite a state or local wildlife specialist or conservation officer to be a guest. Local environmental advocacy groups are another source of local information.

Figures and Tables:

Figure 23.12
Diversity "Hotspots"

Figure 23.13
Victim of Small Population Size

Figure 23.14
Restoration Project

Notes

Biomes and Natural Resources: Where Do You Live? 24

Chapter at a Glance

24.1 Terrestrial Biomes

24.2 Aquatic Biomes

24.3 Human Habitats

Visual Lecture Outline

24.1 Terrestrial Biomes

A. Forests and Shrublands

B. Grasslands

C. Desert

D. Tundra

Key Terms: biome; boreal forest; chaparral; climate; desert; forest; grassland; permafrost; prairie; precipitation; savanna; steppe; temperate forest; tropical forest; tundra; weather

Instructor Resources in Teaching Toolbox: Chapter 24 PPT slides; TAs 431–434, 436

In-Class Activity: *Planet Earth:* There is no better way to excite the class about the diversity of Earth's biomes than by showing parts of the visually breathtaking BBC documentary series *Planet Earth.* I prefer the version narrated by David Attenborough (an American version narrated by Sigourney Weaver also exists). A companion web site exists at http://dsc.discovery.com/convergence/planet-earth/planet-earth.html.

Figures and Tables:

Table 24.1
Factors That Influence Local and Regional Climate

Figure 24.1
Distribution of Earth's Land Biomes

Figure 24.2
Forest Biomes

Figure 24.3
Prairie in Late Summer

Figure 24.4
Tundra

24.2 Aquatic Biomes

A. Freshwater

B. Saltwater

Key Terms: aquatic; coral reef; estuary; freshwater; lake; marine; pond; river; saltwater; wetland

Instructor Resources in Teaching Toolbox: Chapter 24 PPT slides; TA 434

Figures and Tables:

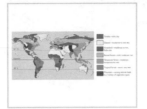

Figure 24.5
Wetlands

Figure 24.6
Coral Reefs

Figure 24.7
Estuary

24.3 Human Habitats

A. Energy and Natural Resources

B. Waste Production

C. Climate Change

D. The Future of Our Shared Environment

Key Terms: ecological footprint; global climate change; greenhouse effect; smog; solid waste; wastewater

Instructor Resources in Teaching Toolbox: Chapter 24 PPT slides; TAs 434-435; *Human Biology Animations:* "Human Population Growth," "Age Structure and Population Growth"; *BLAST! Tutorial:* "The Greenhouse Effect"; *ABC News Video:* "Global Warming"

In-Class Activity: *An Inconvenient Truth:* Viewing and discussion of the film can really motivate students to think about global warming at both personal and planet-wide levels. A companion web site to the film is www.climatecrisis.net/.

Figures and Tables:

Figure 24.8
Human Modification of Earth's Land Surface

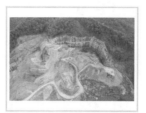

Figure 24.9
Cost of Fossil Fuel Extraction

Figure 24.10
Disposal of Garbage

Figure 24.11
Effect of Waste Gas Emissions

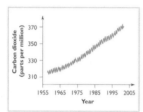

Figure 24.12
Carbon Dioxide Levels in the Atmosphere

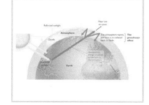

Figure 24.13
Greenhouse Effect

Figure 24.14
Projected Sea Level Rise

Notes

Teaching Tips for First-Time Instructors and Adjunct Professors

How to Be an Effective Teacher

(From David Royse, *Teaching Tips for College and University Instructors: A Practical Guide*, published by Allyn & Bacon, Boston, MA. © 2001 by Pearson Education, Inc. Adapted by permission of the publisher.)

A look at fifty years of research "on the way teachers teach and learners learn" reveals five broad principles of good teaching practice (Chickering and Gamson, 1987).

Five Principles of Good Teaching Practice

1. **Frequent student-faculty contact:** Faculty who are concerned about their students and their progress and who are perceived to be easy to talk to, serve to motivate and keep students involved.

Things you can do to apply this principle:
- Attend events sponsored by students.
- Serve as a mentor or advisor to students.
- Keep "open" or "drop-in" office hours.

2. **The encouragement of cooperation among students:** There is a wealth of research indicating that students benefit from the use of small-group and peer-learning instructional approaches.

Things you can do to apply this principle:
- Have students share in class their interests and backgrounds.
- Create small groups to work on projects together.
- Encourage students to study together.

3. **Prompt feedback:** Learning theory research has consistently shown that the quicker the feedback, the greater the learning.

Things you can do to apply this principle:
- Return quizzes and exams by the next class meeting.
- Return homework within one week.
- Provide students with detailed comments on their written papers.

4. **Emphasize time on task:** This principle refers to the amount of actual involvement with the material being studied and applies, obviously, to the way the instructor uses classroom instructional time. Faculty need good time-management skills.

Things you can do to apply this principle:
- Require students who miss classes to make up lost work.
- Require students to rehearse before making oral presentations.
- Don't let class breaks stretch out too long.

5. **Communicating high expectations:** The key here is not to make the course impossibly difficult but to have goals that can be attained as long as individual learners stretch and work hard, going beyond what they already know.

Things you can do to apply this principle:

- Communicate your expectations orally and in writing at the beginning of the course.
- Explain the penalties for students who turn work in late.
- Identify excellent work by students; display exemplars if possible.

 Tips for Thriving:

CREATING AN INCLUSIVE CLASSROOM

How do you model an open, accepting attitude within your classroom where students will feel it is safe to engage in give-and-take discussions? First, view students as individuals instead of representatives of separate and distinct groups. Cultivate a climate that is respectful of diverse viewpoints, and don't allow ridicule, or defamatory or hurtful remarks. Try to encourage everyone in the class to participate, and be alert to showing favoritism.

Planning Your Course

(From David Royse, *Teaching Tips for College and University Instructors: A Practical Guide,* published by Allyn & Bacon, Boston, MA. © 2001 by Pearson Education, Inc. Adapted by permission of the publisher.)

Constructing the syllabus: The syllabus should clearly communicate course objectives, assignments, required readings, and grading policies. Think of the syllabus as a stand-alone document. Those students who miss the first or second meeting of a class should be able to learn most of what they need to know about the requirements of the course from reading the syllabus. Start by collecting syllabi from colleagues who have recently taught the course you will be teaching and look for common threads and themes.

Problems to avoid: One mistake commonly made by educators teaching a course for the first time is that they may have rich and intricate visions of how they want students to demonstrate comprehension and synthesis of the material, but they somehow fail to convey this information to those enrolled. Check your syllabus to make sure your expectations have been fully articulated. Be very specific. Avoid vaguely worded instructions that can be misinterpreted.

 Tips for Thriving:

VISUAL QUALITY

Students today are highly visual learners, so you should give special emphasis to the visual quality of the materials you provide to students. Incorporate graphics into your syllabus and other handouts. Color code your materials so materials for different sections of the course are on different-colored papers. Such visuals are likely to create a perception among students that you are contemporary.

Your First Class

(From Richard E. Lyons, Marcella L. Kysilka, & George E. Pawlas, *The Adjunct Professor's Guide to Success: Surviving and Thriving In The Classroom,* published by Allyn & Bacon, Boston, MA. © 1999 by Pearson Education, Inc. Adapted by permission of the publisher.)

Success in achieving a great start is almost always directly attributable to the quality and quantity of planning that has been invested by the course professor. If the first meeting of your class is to be successful, you should strive to achieve seven distinct goals.

Seven Goals for a Successful First Meeting

1. **Create a positive first impression:** Renowned communications consultant Roger Ailes claims you have fewer than 10 seconds to create a positive image of yourself. Students are greatly influenced by the visual component; therefore, you must look the part of the professional professor. Dress as you would for a professional job interview. Greet each student entering the room. Be approachable and genuine.

2. **Introduce yourself effectively:** Communicate to students who you are and why you are credible as the teacher of the course. Seek to establish your approachability by "building common ground," such as stating your understanding of students' hectic lifestyles or their common preconceptions toward the subject matter.

3. **Clarify the goals and expectations:** Make a transparency of each page of the syllabus for display on an overhead projector and, using a cover sheet, expose each section as you explain it. Provide clarification and elicit questions.

4. **Conduct an activity that introduces students to each other:** Students' chances of being able to complete a course effectively are enhanced if each comes to perceive the classmates as a "support network." The small amount of time you invest in an icebreaker will help create a positive classroom atmosphere and pay additional dividends throughout the term.

5. **Learn students' names:** A student who is regularly addressed by name feels more valued, is invested more effectively in classroom discussion, and will approach the professor with questions and concerns.

6. **Whet students' appetite for the course material:** The textbook adopted for the course is critical to your success. Your first meeting should include a review of its approach, features, and sequencing. Explain to students what percentage of class tests will be derived from material from the textbook.

7. **Reassure students of the value of the course:** At the close of your first meeting reassure students that the course will be a valuable learning experience and a wise investment of their time. Review the reasons why the course is a good investment: important and relevant content, interesting classmates, and a dynamic classroom environment.

Strategies for Teaching and Learning

(From David Royse, *Teaching Tips for College and University Instructors: A Practical Guide,* published by Allyn & Bacon, Boston, MA. © 2001 by Pearson Education, Inc. Adapted by permission of the publisher.)

Team learning: The essential features of this small-group learning approach, developed originally for use in large college classrooms, are (1) relatively permanent heterogeneous task groups; (2) grading based on a combination of individual performance, group performance, and peer evaluation; (3) organization of the course so that the majority of class time is spent on small-group activities; and (4) a six-step instructional process similar to the following model:

1. Individual study of material outside of the class is assigned.
2. Individual testing is used (multiple-choice questions over homework at the beginning of class).
3. Groups discuss their answers and then are given a group test of the same items. They then get immediate feedback (answers).
4. Groups may prepare written appeals of items.
5. Feedback is given from instructor.
6. An application-oriented activity is assigned (e.g., a problem to be solved requiring input from all group members).

If you plan to use team learning in your class, inform students at the beginning of the course of your intentions to do so and explain the benefits of small-group learning. Foster group cohesion by sitting groups together and letting them choose "identities" such as a team name or slogan. You will need to structure and supervise the groups and ensure that the projects build on newly acquired learning. Make the projects realistic and interesting and ensure that they are adequately structured so that each member's contribution is 25 percent. Students should be given criteria by which they can assess and evaluate the contributions of their peers on a project-by-project basis (Michaelsen, 1994).

 Tips for Thriving:

ACTIVE LEARNING AND LECTURING

Lecturing is one of the most time-honored teaching methods, but does it have a place in an active learning environment? There are times when lecturing can be effective. Think about the following when planning a lecture:

Build interest: Capture your students' attention by leading off with an anecdote or cartoon.

Maximize understanding and retention: Use brief handouts and demonstrations as a visual backup to enable your students to see as well as hear.

Involve students during the lecture: Interrupt the lecture occasionally to challenge students to answer spot quiz questions.

Reinforce the lecture: Give students a self-scoring review test at the end of the lecture.

Grading and Assessment Techniques

(From Philip C. Wankat, *The Effective, Efficient Professor: Teaching Scholarship and Service*, published by Allyn & Bacon, Boston, MA. © 2002 by Pearson Education, Inc. Adapted by permission of the publisher.)

Philosophy of grading: Develop your own philosophy of grading by picturing in your mind the performance of typical A students, B students, and so on. Try different grading methods until you find one that fits your philosophy and is reasonably fair. Always look closely at students on grade borders—take into account personal factors if the group is small. Be consistent with or slightly more generous than the procedure outlined in your syllabus.

Criterion grading: Professor Philip Wankat writes: "I currently use a form of criterion grading for my sophomore and junior courses. I list the scores in the syllabus that will guarantee the students A's, B's, and so forth. For example, a score of 85 to 100 guarantees an A; 75 to 85, a B; 65 to 75, a C; and 55 to 65, a D. If half the class gets above 85% they all get an A. This reduces competition and allows students to work together and help each other. The standard grade gives students something to aim for and tells them exactly what their grade is at any time. For students whose net scores are close to the borders at the end of the course, I look at other factors before deciding a final grade, such as attendance."

 Tips for Thriving:

RESULT FEEDBACK

As stated earlier, feedback on results is the most effective of motivating factors. Anxious students are especially hungry for positive feedback. You can quickly and easily provide it by simply writing "Great job!" on the answer sheets or tests. For students who didn't perform well, a brief note such as "I'd love to talk with you at the end of class" can be especially reassuring. The key is to be proactive and maintain high standards, while requiring students to retain ownership of their success.

Managing Problem Situations

(From Philip C. Wankat, *The Effective, Efficient Professor: Teaching, Scholarship and Service*, published by Allyn & Bacon, Boston, MA. © 2002 by Pearson Education, Inc. Adapted by permission of the publisher.)

Cheating: Cheating is one behavior that should not be tolerated. Tolerating cheating tends to make it worse. Prevention of cheating is much more effective than trying to cure it once it has occurred. A professor can prevent cheating by:

- Creating rapport with students
- Gaining a reputation for giving fair tests
- Giving clear instructions and guidelines before, during, and after tests
- Educating students on the ethics of plagiarism
- Requiring periodic progress reports and outlines before a paper is due

Try to develop exams that are perceived as fair and secure by students. Often, the accusation that certain questions were tricky is valid as it relates to ambiguous language and trivial material. Ask your mentor or an experienced instructor to closely review the final draft of your first few exams for these factors.

(From David Royse, *Teaching Tips for College and University Instructors: A Practical Guide*, published by Allyn & Bacon, Boston, MA. © 2001 by Pearson Education, Inc. Adapted by permission of the publisher.)

Unmotivated students: There are numerous reasons why students may not be motivated. The "required course" scenario is a likely explanation—although politics in colonial America is your life's work, it is safe to assume that not everyone will share your enthusiasm. There are also personal reasons such as a death of a loved one or depression. Whenever you detect a pattern that you assume to be due to lack of motivation (e.g., missing classes, not handing assignments in on time, nonparticipation in class), arrange a time to have the student meet with you outside the classroom. Candidly express your concerns and then listen.

 Tips for Thriving:

DISCIPLINE

One effective method for dealing with some discipline problems is to ask the class for feedback (Angelo & Cross, 1993). In a one-minute quiz, ask the students, "What can I do to help you learn?" Collate the responses and present them to the class. If behavior such as excessive talking appears in some responses (e.g., "Tell people to shut up"), this gives you the backing to ask students to be quiet. Use of properly channeled peer pressure is often effective in controlling undesired behavior.

Motivating students is part of the faculty members' job. To increase motivation, professors should show enthusiasm for the topic, use various media and methods to present material, use humor in the classroom, employ activities that encourage active learning, and give frequent, positive feedback.

(From Sharon Baiocco, & Jamie N. De Waters, *Successful College Teaching: Problem Solving Strategies of Distinguished Professors*, published by Allyn & Bacon, Boston, MA. © 1998 by Pearson Education, Inc. Adapted by permission of the publisher.)

Credibility problems: If you are an inexperienced instructor, you may have problems with students not taking you seriously. At the first class meeting, articulate clear rules of classroom decorum and conduct yourself with dignity and respect for students. Try to exude that you are in charge and are the "authority" and avoid trying to pose as the students' friend.

Improving Your Performance

(From Richard E. Lyons, Marcella L. Kysilka, & George E. Pawlas, *The Adjunct Professor's Guide to Success: Surviving and Thriving In The Classroom*, published by Allyn & Bacon, Boston, MA. © 1999 by Pearson Education, Inc. Adapted by permission of the publisher.)

Self-evaluation: The instructor who regularly engages in systematic self-evaluation will unquestionably derive greater reward from the formal methods of evaluation commonly employed by colleges and universities. One method for providing structure to an ongoing system of self-evaluation is to keep a journal of reflections on your teaching experiences. Regularly invest 15 or 20 introspective minutes following each class meeting to focus especially on the strategies and events in class that you feel could be improved. Committing your thoughts and emotions to writing enables you to develop more effective habits, build confidence in your teaching performance, and make more effective comparisons later. The following questions will help guide self-assessment:

How do I typically begin a class?
Where/How do I position myself in the class?
How do I move in the classroom?
Where are my eyes usually focused?
Do I facilitate students' visual processing of course material?
Do I change the speed, volume, energy, and tone of my voice?
How do I ask questions of students?
How often, and when, do I smile or laugh in class?

How do I react when students are inattentive?

How do I react when students disagree or challenge what I say?

How do I typically end a class?

 Tips for Thriving:

VIDEO-RECORDING YOUR CLASS

In recent years, a wide range of professionals have markedly improved their job performance by employing video recorders in their preparation efforts. As an instructor, an effective method might be to ask your mentor or another colleague to tape a 10- to 15-minute mini-lesson, then to debrief it using the assessment questions above. Critiquing a videotaped session provides objectivity and is therefore more likely to effect change. Involving a colleague as an informal coach will enable you to gain from that person's experience and perspective and will reduce the chances of your engaging in self-depreciation.

References

Ailes, R. (1996). *You are the message: Getting what you want by being who you are.* New York: Doubleday.

Chickering, A. W., & Gamson, Z. F. (1987). "Seven principles for good practice in undergraduate education." *AAHE Bulletin, 39,* 3–7.

Michaelson, L. K. (1994). Team learning: Making a case for the small-group option. In K. W. Prichard & R. M. Sawyer (Eds.), *Handbook of college teaching.* Westport, CT: Greenwood Press.

Sorcinelli, M. D. (1991). Research findings on the seven principles. In A. W. Chickering & Z. Gamson (Eds.), "Applying the seven principles of good practice in undergraduate education." *New Directions for Teaching and Learning 47.* San Francisco: Jossey-Bass.

Notes:

Biology 000
Human Biology Spring Semester

Course Syllabus

Instructor:	XXX
Office:	XXX
Phone:	415-555-1111
E-mail:	xxx@XXX.edu
Office Hours:	Monday–Friday 10:00–11:00 am
Text:	Belk/Borden, *Human Biology*; ISBN 013148124X
Lab Manual:	Gunstream, *Biological Explorations: A Human Approach*, 6th edition; ISBN 0131560727

I. **Lecture**   A tentative lecture schedule is attached. You are responsible for all material in the assigned chapters as well as the material presented in class. If you must miss a lecture, it is **your** responsibility to obtain the notes from a classmate. Attendance in lecture is vital to your success and is part of your grade evaluation.

II. **Lab**   You are required to **fully** attend each lab. You will receive **NO** points for a lab that you did not attend (no make-ups, no exceptions)! A laboratory schedule is attached. You should be adequately prepared for each laboratory period; this includes reading the laboratory exercise **before** the laboratory period.

III. **Safety**   Laboratory safety is of paramount importance. It is essential that you follow proper procedures at all times. **No food, drink, tobacco, or gum** is permitted in the lab. Read and commit to memory the laboratory safety material in the lab book.

IV. **Web Site**   www.school.edu/instructors/instructorname/ (sample)
The pertinent course information is also posted on my faculty web site. This site may be used throughout the semester to post information and assignments. Links to other science-oriented web sites of interest are also provided.

V. **Grading**   There will be four written exams (100 points each) and a comprehensive final (200 points). The laboratory performance will be evaluated by participation, lab reports, and quizzes (specifics will be announced). Lab reports are to be turned in at the beginning of the next lab period. Reports turned in late will receive reduced credit. **You must pass both the lecture and laboratory components of the course to pass the course!!**

Grades will be assigned based on percentage of total points earned:

A	90–100%
B	80–89%
C	70–79%
D	60–69%
F	<60%

Tentative point breakdown:

Lecture Exams	400
Final	200
Lab Attendance/Reports/Quizzes	≈ 170
Attendance, Attitude, and Participation	30
Total Points	≈ 800

VI. **Policy on Missed Exams, Quizzes, and Labs NO** makeup labs or quizzes will be given. **One** missed exam can be made up by adding the appropriate number of points missed to the value of the final exam. Example: If one unit test is missed, the final for that person will be worth 200 pts (value of final) + 100 pts (value of missed exam) = 300 pts.

Biology 000 Laboratory Schedule
Spring Semester

Week	Lab
1	Orientation (Ex. #)/The Microscope (Ex. #)
2	The Cell (Ex. #)/Diffusion and Osmosis (Ex. #)
3	Cell Division (Ex. #)
4	Organization of the Human Body (Ex. #)
5	Support and Movement (Ex. #)
6	Circulation of the Blood (Ex. #)/Blood (Ex. #)
7	Digestion (Ex. #)
8	Gas Exchange (Ex. #)
9	Excretion (Ex. #)
10	Neural Control (Ex. #)
11	**Spring Break!!!!!!!!!**
12	Sensory Perception (Ex. #)
13	Heredity (Ex. #)
14	Reproduction (Ex. #)
15	Fertilization and Development (Ex. #)
16	Population Growth (Ex. #)

[*Note:* These are sample exercises chosen to correspond with the preceding syllabus. There are additional exercises that may be more pertinent to your class, as well as different exercises that can be applied to the same chapters. These exercises can be rearranged to correspond to your preferred lecture schedule.]

Biology 000
Tentative Lecture Schedule
Human Biology Lecture Schedule (16-week semester)

Week	Topic(s)	Chapter(s)
1	The Scientific Method	1
	Chemistry of Life	2
2	Chemistry of Life (cont.)	2
	Cell Structure and Metabolism	3
3	Cell Structure and Metabolism (cont.)	3
	Genes—Transcription, Translation, Mutation, and Cloning	4
4	Tissues, Organs, and Organ Systems	5
5	**Exam I (Units I and II/Chapters 1–5)**	
	The Musculoskeletal System	6
	The Digestive System	7
6	The Blood	8
	The Cardiovascular System	9
7	The Respiratory System	10
	The Urinary System	11
8	**Exam II (Unit III/Chapters 6–11)**	
	Immune System, Bacteria, Viruses, and Other Pathogens	12
9	Sexually Transmitted Infections	13
	Brain Structure and Function	14
10	The Senses	15
	The Endocrine System	16
11	**Exam III (Unit IV/Chapters 12–16)**	
	DNA Synthesis, Mitosis, and Meiosis	17
12	Human Reproduction	18
	Heredity	19
13	Extensions of Mendelism, Sex Linkage, Pedigree Analysis, and DNA Fingerprinting	20
	Development and Aging	21
14	**Exam IV (Unit V/Chapters 17–21)**	
	Evolution	22
15	Population, Community, and Ecosystem Ecology	23
	Ecosystems and Biomes	24
16	**Final Exam**	

Support Services	
Accommodations	Insert school-specific information
Services for students with disabilities	Insert school-specific information
Academic and educational advising	Insert school-specific web site address
Career counseling	Insert school-specific web site address
Library	Insert school-specific web site address for school library and location of library, and tutorial sessions held there, etc.
Academic achievement center	Insert school-specific information (web site, phone number, services provided, hours, link to a campus map, etc.)
Computer labs	Insert school-specific information (web site, phone number, services provided, hours, link to a campus map, etc.)

Disclaimer

"This syllabus is representative of materials that will be covered in this class; it is not a contract between the student and the institution. It is subject to change without notice. Any potential exceptions to stated policies and requirements will be addressed on an individual basis, and only for reasons that meet specific requirements. If you have any problems related to this class, please feel free to discuss them with me."

Biology 000
Human Biology Summer Semester

Course Syllabus

Instructor:	XXX
Office:	XXX
Phone:	415-555-1111
E-mail:	xxx@XXX.edu
Office Hours:	Monday–Friday 10:00–11:00 am
Text:	Belk/Borden, *Human Biology*; ISBN 013148124X
Lab Manual:	Gunstream, *Biological Explorations: A Human Approach*, 6th edition; ISBN 0131560727

I. **Lecture**   A tentative lecture schedule is attached. You are responsible for all material in the assigned chapters as well as the material presented in class. If you must miss a lecture, it is **your** responsibility to obtain the notes from a classmate. Attendance in lecture is vital to your success and is part of your grade evaluation.

II. **Lab**   You are required to **fully** attend each lab. You will receive **NO** points for a lab that you did not attend (no make-ups, no exceptions)! A laboratory schedule is attached. You should be adequately prepared for each laboratory period; this includes reading the laboratory exercise **before** the laboratory period.

III. **Safety**   Laboratory safety is of paramount importance. It is essential that you follow proper procedures at all times. **No food, drink, tobacco, or gum** is permitted in the lab. Read and commit to memory the laboratory safety material in the lab book.

IV. **Web Site**   www.school.edu/instructors/instructorname/ (sample)

The pertinent course information is also posted on my faculty web site. This site may be used throughout the semester to post information and assignments. Links to other science-oriented web sites of interest are also provided.

V. **Grading**   There will be four written exams (100 points each) and a comprehensive final (200 points). The laboratory performance will be evaluated by participation, lab reports, and quizzes (specifics will be announced). Lab reports are to be turned in at the beginning of the next lab period. Reports turned in late will receive reduced credit. **You must pass both the lecture and laboratory components of the course to pass the course!!**

Grades will be assigned based on percentage of total points earned:

A	90–100%
B	80–89%
C	70–79%
D	60–69%
F	<60%

Tentative point breakdown:

Lecture Exams	400
Final	200
Lab Attendance/Reports/Quizzes	≈ 170
Attendance, Attitude, and Participation	30
Total Points	≈ 800

VI.   **Policy on Missed Exams, Quizzes, and Labs NO** makeup labs or quizzes will be given. One missed exam can be made up by adding the appropriate number of points missed to the value of the final exam. Example: If one unit test is missed, the final for that person will be worth 200 pts (value of final) + 100 pts (value of missed exam) = 300 pts.

Biology 000 Laboratory Schedule
Summer Semester

Week	Lab
1	Orientation (Ex. #)/The Microscope (Ex. #)
2	The Cell (Ex. #)/Diffusion and Osmosis (Ex. #)
3	Support and Movement (Ex. #)/Digestion (Ex. #)
4	Circulation of the Blood (Ex. #)/Blood (Ex. #)
5	Gas Exchange (Ex. #)
6	Excretion (Ex. #)/Neural Control (Ex. #)
7	Sensory Perception (Ex. #)
8	Reproduction (Ex. #)
9	Heredity (Ex. #)
10	Human Evolution (Ex. #)/Population Growth (Ex. #)

[*Note:* These are sample exercises chosen to correspond with the preceding syllabus. There are additional exercises that may be more pertinent to your class, as well as different exercises that can be applied to the same chapters. These exercises can be rearranged to correspond to your preferred lecture schedule.]

Biology 000
Tentative Lecture Schedule
Human Biology Lecture Schedule (10-week semester)

Week	Topic(s)	Chapter(s)
1	The Scientific Method	1
	Chemistry of Life	2
	Cell Structure and Metabolism	3
2	Genes—Transcription, Translation, Mutation, and Cloning	4
	Tissues, Organs, and Organ Systems	5
3	The Musculoskeletal System	6
	The Digestive System	7
4	The Blood	8
	The Cardiovascular System	9
5	The Respiratory System	10
	The Urinary System	11
	Midterm Exam (Units I–III/Chapters 1–11)	
6	Immune System, Bacteria, Viruses, and Other Pathogens	12
	Sexually Transmitted Infections	13
	Brain Structure and Function	14
7	The Senses	15
	The Endocrine System	16
8	DNA Synthesis, Mitosis, and Meiosis	17
	Human Reproduction	18
	Heredity	19
9	Extensions of Mendelism, Sex Linkage, Pedigree Analysis, and DNA Fingerprinting	20
	Development and Aging	21
	Evolution	22
10	Population, Community, and Ecosystem Ecology	23
	Ecosystems and Biomes	24

Final Exam (Units IV–VI/Chapters 12–24)
Final Examination

Section A	Wednesday	May 3	9:30–11:45 am
Section C	Wednesday	May 3	12:00– 2:15 pm

Support Services	
Accommodations	Insert school-specific information
Services for students with disabilities	Insert school-specific information
Academic and educational advising	Insert school-specific web site address
Career counseling	Insert school-specific web site address
Library	Insert school-specific web site address for school library and location of library, and tutorial sessions held there, etc.
Academic achievement center	Insert school-specific information (web site, phone number, services provided, hours, link to a campus map, etc.)
Computer labs	Insert school-specific information (web site, phone number, services provided, hours, link to a campus map, etc.)

Disclaimer

"This syllabus is representative of materials that will be covered in this class; it is not a contract between the student and the institution. It is subject to change without notice. Any potential exceptions to stated policies and requirements will be addressed on an individual basis, and only for reasons that meet specific requirements. If you have any problems related to this class, please feel free to discuss them with me."

Using CourseCompass™

The CourseCompass™ software series is a set of online course materials meant to be used as an online class or as a complement to any health and wellness course. Materials can be customized to provide your students with preloaded course materials or with course contents you load for them.

To begin with CourseCompass™, you will need to register. If this is your first time using CourseCompass™, you will need an instructor access code, which can be obtained by clicking on Request Instructor Access on www.coursecompass.com. You will be walked through the process.

After logging in for the first time, you will be taken to the My CourseCompass™ page. Creating a course is quite simple: you can search for your text by ISBN or discipline, and your course will be created in about 24 hours.

Course Compass for Human Biology offers premium online content, including *ABC News* Videos, Human Biology Animations, textbook quizzes, glossary flashcards, and a link to downloadable instructor resources like BioFlix movies, Interactive Physiology for Human Biology slides, and electronic files of the Instructor Guide and Test Bank. Once students are logged into the CourseCompass™ site, they are also set up in a CourseCompass™ gradebook, which will automatically record all scores and assignments completed through CourseCompass™.

This primer gives a brief introduction to CourseCompass™, providing an overview of how to integrate these resources into your course (from navigating the actual program to providing assignments for classroom sessions) to using CourseCompass™ to enhance lecture content and assign student homework assignments.

The Practical Aspects

After creating your CourseCompass™ log in, you will need to log in again to customize your course. When you log in, it opens to the My CourseCompass™ page. CourseCompass™ is organized by four areas that appear on the page: My CourseCompass, Courses, Need Help?, and Products & Resources. Your course will appear on the My CourseCompass™ page under the Courses heading. To create your course, just click on Create/Copy Course and follow the simple directions.

Most of the setup and customization is initiated from the Control Panel (the tab on the bottom left of the Courses page). These Control Panel items are visible to you, but not your students.

Working with the Control Panel

Content Areas

The content area of the Control Panel includes Course Information, Chapter Contents, Study Tools, Assignments, and Instructor Resources. In Course Information, you will find the software requirements to run CourseCompass™ and downloads if needed.

Course Documents (preloaded)

The items loaded into chapter contents include text-based resources, everything chapter practice quizzes, Human Biology Animations with quizzes, glossary flashcards, crossword puzzles, and *ABC News Videos*. These items can be modified or removed for use in your class or assigned for homework. Chapter practice quizzes are particularly useful as homework assignments to reinforce chapter comprehension. Video clips are available here and are excellent tools to introduce your topics in lecture.

In addition, the Human Biology in the News features include up-to-the-minute news feeds from respected science news sources. The accompanying essay questions can be useful as a lecture starter or as a homework assignment that brings current science topics into the classroom.

Internet resources such as ResearchNavigator.com, an electronic database that provides access to scholarly journals and other valuable Internet resource sites, are also accessible through this section.

Assignments/External Links

The remaining content areas, such as Assignments and Instructor Resources, are not preloaded and are places for instructors to load personal course assignment instructions or links. A nice use for this area is to load any assignment instruction sheets, review sheets, and/or your PowerPoint lectures for student viewing. One common idea for classrooms that allow it is to have students download your PowerPoint lectures and take notes directly on the slides. However, you could also simply encourage students to view your lectures on their own at home or at a library computer as a review for upcoming tests.

An example of how to use both assignments and external links is to load your PowerPoint lecture from the external links section (or from the companion web site for instructor resources at www.aw-bc.com) and include an assignment to complete after viewing the PowerPoint lecture. For example, the Chapter 9 (The Cardiovascular System) PowerPoint lecture begins with a Human Biology Animation; after students view this, ask them to answer a worksheet loaded by you into the Assignments section or to take the premade quiz that follows each animation. This can be printed out and brought to class or sent to you directly via email for grading. You can also have students put it in the Digital Dropbox for your viewing later.

Course Tools

This area of CourseCompass™ allows you to personalize your content and create a course calendar. Each section may or may not be made available to your students to use for e-mail, handing in assignments (Digital Dropbox), or obtaining staff information (this is an area where you may want to post your vitae or short biography). If you use CourseCompass™ as a stand-alone online course, this area works well for classroom management. When CourseCompass™ is purely a complement to your lecture classes, you may choose to remove many of these options. Be careful not to overload your course page with unnecessary items that may distract students from the required content and assignments for your course. The area that may be most beneficial is Send Email, so that students can be reminded of tests, assignments, or class cancellations.

The Announcement area is another important area, and you may want to use it as your opening page. Instructors can change it at regular intervals and update all assignment information, class lecture content, and test information. Instructors can also describe the weekly assignments and readings due and any other announcements regarding class.

The Discussion Board is particularly useful for bringing students together to discuss, among themselves (either anonymously or by name), controversial issues or topics. A forum can be posted for students to write about and reply to other students with comments. This is valuable to use when a class discussion is not finished or needs more exploration. The discussion responses can be organized alphabetically and printed out for grading at any time. They can also be stored as an archive for viewing at a later date.

Course Options

The Manage Course Menu and Manage Tools areas are found in this section. This is where to choose which icons (on the tool bar) you will make available to your students and how you will display them. Remember to not overload students and to only post the items you will be using in your course (i.e., do not make the Digital Dropbox available if you want your students to hand in assignments in class only). You can also use this area to add any other icon or materials to the course. For example, this is where you may load the PowerPoint lectures you use in class so students can refer to these when studying for tests or obtain lecture notes if they missed class. You may want to name this tool Lecture Notes or something similar, and it will be placed in the tool area of CourseCompass™ as a separate icon.

User Management

This tool enhances group project work and provides necessary group project materials for all students to access and/or store their work for group members to view or to work together.

Assessment

An excellent tool for instructors to use for administering tests, surveying students, and storing grades. CourseCompass™ automatically posts grades from quizzes and other assessments, which saves instructors a lot of grading time. TestGen can create a random test for you, you can choose which questions to use, or you can add your own questions.

Help

This area is for instructors to access technical support and CourseCompass™ help. You can also visit the My CourseCompass™ and click on Getting Started with CourseCompass™ to access the How Do I? feature, which walks you through many CourseCompass™ applications.

CourseCompass™ in the Classroom

Enhancing Classroom Learning

After navigating the Control Panel, you can now plan some ways to use this in your class. CourseCompass™ can be used both as a classroom supplement and as a stand-alone online class for students to use to access class materials and complete assignments.

One of the most useful tools on CourseCompass™ is the *ABC News* Videos. You can access these videos from your laptop and then easily open your Power Point slides to start the lecture.

Another useful way to use CourseCompass™ in class is to build flashcards for your lecture to close your lecture content at the end. Have students work in pairs to find the definition of the term and raise their hand if they know the answer. You might also show the definition card and have them try to find the term instead. The flashcards are found in the Study Tools section.

The *ABC News* Videos and the flashcards are only two ways that CourseCompass™ can enhance student involvement and learning in the classroom. Be sure to spend some time looking around CourseCompass™ to see how you can best tailor it to your course and your students.

CourseCompass™ Online Course Only

Setting up an online class takes time because course materials need to be updated frequently and the assignments need to reflect the new content. Having said this, the preloaded content of CourseCompass™ makes this task somewhat easier. The challenge is to choose materials that equate to the required time per unit at your school and to offer an online class experience that provides some interaction and teacher involvement. For example, for a three-semester unit class, the estimated hours of work for a student is 3 in class hours/week and approximately 2 to 3 study hours outside class. Therefore, when a student is taking your class online, they need to spend 5 to 6 hours/week working on the assignments and readings for this class.

To make classroom management easiest, an online class should correspond closely to a face-to-face class so students can use them interchangeably. Course planning is easier when your classes are all doing the same assignments. Online teaching is a new territory for many instructors. It is harder to interact with the class and to integrate your teaching styles into the online format. In some ways, online teaching allows for more individual teaching (through email) and thus allows for a more "intimate" or personalized experience; yet, students do not get to work closely with each other as they do in a classroom setting. There are pros and cons to online classes; here are some suggestions that will help your online course be the best it can be.

Orientation

To best allow students to succeed in an online class, you may want to require an introductory face-to-face orientation so the two of you can enroll in CourseCompass™; browse the site; and download the syllabus, assignments, and calendar together. Students tend to have issues with access codes, plug-ins, or system requirements with their home computers; thus, this orientation is crucial. You may suggest that students set up a "virtual" classroom at home with their computer and a physical bulletin board with the syllabus, assignments, discussion items, calendar, and quizzes for each chapter on it. This way, each week they can refer to a hard copy of the discussion, assignments, or quizzes. They can work on them at other times throughout the day and answer them first on paper before submitting them for grading. If a face-to-face orientation is impossible, students can be directed to the Support Center or you can walk them through the process over the phone.

During orientation, you may choose to do a class exercise for students to get to know each other and begin to relate as a class online. For example, you can have them respond to a discussion item of your choosing (you can use the scenarios in the Course Documents under Discussion Forum in each lesson). Students can then see who everyone is and begin to feel more comfortable navigating the site and interacting with each other online.

Weekly Announcements

This section is what you may want to use for your opening page. Students see these on the first page when they open CourseCompass™. Here is where you can post the required class assignments, readings, and due dates. For example:

Week of MM/DD/YY

1) Please read Chapter 1 and answer the two multiple-choice quizzes and case studies, due Friday at 2 pm. Case studies need to be submitted to the Digital Dropbox. Quizzes are graded and recorded automatically when you click on Submit.
2) Assignment X is also due next week; remember to review the assignment instructions under the Assignments section. You should be working on this.
3) Discussion item is also posted, and comments are due on Friday by 2 pm.

Sample assignments may require students to view the *ABC News* Videos for a certain chapter and answer questions you have posted, to be placed in the Digital Dropbox or emailed to you directly. Or, for example, you could have students work through the Immune System for Chapter 12 on the Interactive Physiology for Human Biology CD, and complete the worksheets for Chapter 12.

Quizzes

You can have students take both multiple-choice tests 1 and 2 for at least one chapter (sometimes two chapters) each week or at other regular intervals. These tests are automatically graded and organized in your gradebook section in CourseCompass™. This helps instructors determine whether if students are reading the texts and understanding the terms and concepts. Students can print these out and work on them in hard copy before submitting them online. Therefore, they are "open book tests." Each multiple-choice quiz is answered and submitted, and the correct answers can be viewed. You can set it up in the Assignments section so that students can only take the test once. This way, students can view the tests, but once they take the test, they are done. You can also load a TestGen test here, which can be scored and submitted directly to the gradebook.

Discussion

You can require students to respond and reply (to at least one other person) to a discussion topic related to the weekly course content. To allow students some time to think about these topics, you may want to post all discussion items at the beginning of the semester, so students can print these out and think about them from hard copy before replying. Sometimes these discussions require outside research. If a group project is required, students can join up to do them by discussing the project in this area.

There are some good questions for discussion and reflection found in the end of each chapter and after the *ABC News* Videos. Other sample discussion questions, and their answers, can be found in the *Instructor Guide for Human Biology* by Donald Glassman.

Allowing anonymous posting on discussion items may allow for more sharing of information. However, with this option, instructors do not know which students have participated, so points cannot be assigned. You may want to use this anonymous posting option for sensitive issues (i.e., STIs, discussions on health problems from smoking), so students feel free to talk without being judged.

Assignments

Instructions for assignment formats, requirements, and submission are all loaded into the Assignments section.

Group assignments can be done by using the Manage Group section under User Management in the Control Panel. You can set up group discussion boards and group sharing through this section, and later see what work was done by whom.

For research assignments, students can click on the ResearchNavigator.com link on the My CourseCompass™ opening page, under Products and Resources. Here students have access to EBSCO Academic Journal and Abstract Database, the *New York Times* Search by Subject™ Archive, Link Library, and *The Financial Times* Article Archive and Company Financials, all databases designed to get the research project started.

The *Instructor Guide for Human Biology*, included in your Teaching Toolbox, has a number of possible assignments for every chapter that you can tailor to work in CourseCompass™. Once you understand the basics, any assignment can be added to CourseCompass™.

Notes

Notes

Notes

Notes

Notes

Notes

Notes

Notes

Notes

Notes

Notes

Notes